LITTLE STAR 7

a journal of poetry and prose

HOWARD ALTMANN

MALCOLM BARRETT

APRIL BERNARD

NINA BOGIN

MARIN BUSCHEL

TADEUSZ DĄBROWSKI

GRO DAHLE

RON DE MARIS

BOB ELMENDORF

BARRY GIFFORD

ARIELLE GREENBERG

GILES HARVEY

FRIEDRICH HÖLDERLIN

MARY JO SALTER

CYNAN JONES

GEORGE KALOGERIS

BOŻENA KEFF

MICHAEL KIMBALL

JOSEFINE KLOUGART

STEVE KRONEN

KAREN LEONA ANDERSON

ANTHONY MADRID

QUENTIN MAHONEY

GLYN MAXWELL

JEAN McGARRY

JOHN MORAN

LES MURRAY

ESTER NAOMI PERQUIN

E.O. NESSUNA

MICHAEL PALMER

GLEN POURCIAU

ELLIOT REED

ROWAN RICARDO PHILLIPS

GRACE SCHULMAN

TRAVIS SMITH

MARIA STEPANOVA

JAMES STOTTS

ELIZABETH T. GRAY JR.

JULIA THACKER

AARON THIER

ERICK VERRAN

DEREK WALCOTT

ROSANNA WARREN

SUSAN WHEELER

ROBERT WRIGLEY

ERICA X EISEN

MATT ZAMBITO

SERHIY ZHADAN

Edited by ANN KJELLBERG

IN MEMORY OF DEREK ALTON WALCOTT (1930–2017)

With gratitude to Civitella Ranieri for their support while this issue was in process and particular thanks to this year's authors for their patience

Little Star is an annual journal of poetry and prose. Sign up to receive special offers and order back issues at littlestarjournal.com, or by mail at 107 Bank Street, New York, NY 10014. Current issues are $14.95, plus $4.00 for postage and handling ($10.00 international). See order form on page 381.

Consult our web site to find our customized bookshop, news of Little Star, and other features: littlestarjournal.com.

Editor: ANN KJELLBERG

Assistant: NICK BINNETTE

Contributing Editor: MELISSA GREEN

Typography: JOHN THORP

Interior Design Format: BTDNYC

Cover Design: COULLY TRAORE

Distributed by Ubiquity

Printed by Sterling Pierce Company, East Rockaway, New York

Little Star

107 Bank Street, New York, NY 10014

littlestarjournal.com, info@littlestarjournal.com

Submissions welcome; post preferred

© 2017

Acknowledgments appear on page 380.

ISSN 2151-8637 (print)   ISSN 2158-5830 (digital)

But soon, I'm told, I'll lose my epaulets altogether
and dwindle into a little star.

—JOSEPH BRODSKY (1940–1996)

CONTENTS

TRAVIS SMITH

The Mulberry Novel

It is June. A boy sits next to a mulberry bush,
reading a blue novel. Yet when he reads the final chapter,
the novel will not close, but grows new pages—
pages in the beginning, middle, and end—
and the mulberry bush grows new branches.

He begins to read again. A royal maze-maker
is unlucky in love, and his mazes are too simple
to satisfy the demanding duke.
This was not mentioned before, the boy notices.

The novel now includes a digression,
pages long, comparing windmills to octopi,
giant, terrestrial, stiff-armed octopi.
It includes a traveling harpist and her daughter
who know only the language of harps.

And the orchid smuggler rides the steamship home,
his Ribbonroots and Dragons packed in trunks,
pitying the tobacco merchant, who carries no such secrets;
and the boy reads on, to the end of the novel
which is the flourishing of the next novel, containing the old,
as the mulberry bush contains its old branches.
Now, through the gaps between leaves, you can glimpse him,
your eyes wandering to the newest pages.

Here is the description of a seaside town,
with its gazebos, bathing huts, and old cannons,
here are the triumphs of the knife-throwing girl
and the failure of the ice collector,
the lovers meeting in the cyclorama,
the catalogue of starfish, the chapter of regrets,
and through it all you can no longer see the boy,
and it is June, and you are just beginning to read.

Bring Me the Book of Overturned Laws

He was a philologist with an ornithology habit,
a gumshoe with a hard-on,
an omnigatherum with a grudge.
He was a houseboat habitué.
He could serve as a sundial
in the right kind of light.
He was an antiques dealer on the lam
and his client needed the Magna Carta, and quick.

He screwed on his hat,
checked his gauges and dials, got in the car.
He tracked his mark to a road
marked Disappearing Road. He turned right.
He disappeared. Which happened often
and no longer surprised him.

Table of Abbreviations

ARF	Artificial Rain Fund
BOP	Ban On Pyramids
BST	Boomerang Surveillance Training
C	Crizzle
C2	Cuckooflower
CAAW	Cautious As A Waterbug
DDA	Dictionary Decoding Algorithm
DOCCOTP	Dollop of Cream Cheese On That, Please
EDANSAIMY	Each Day a New Statue Appears In My Yard
EPM	Extremely Painful Memory
FR	Fox's Razor
GWOE	Global War On Eagles
HVT	High Value Tentacle
IP	Ice-Plant
JCRT	Jacobin Calendar Reinstatement Team
KEA	Kudzu Encoding Algorithm
LAG!LAG!	Launch All Ghosts! Launch All Ghosts!
LDF	Langage Des Fleurs
MAD	Mutually Assured Dinner
NVC	National Vortex Commander
OFCT	Observe, Flee, Cower, Tremble
PATLAD	Pity About The Leopards All Dying
QC	Quetzalcoatl Club
RP	Red Pimpernel
SP	Scarlet Pimpernel
SQD	Squellette Qui Danse
TP	Taupe Protocol

UA	Unsupervised Automaton
VIU	Vortex Integration Unit
WWRS	Walt Whitman Resurrection Squad
WWC-RS	Walt Whitman Counter-Resurrection Squad
X	Xebek
YB	Yam Bomb
ZPRTF	Zeno's Paradox Resolution Task Force

CYNAN JONES

The Rabbit

The two boys had come along and found the rabbit dying by the bank. The breeze was up a little and it was nice because it had been dry for so long, and still; and the rabbit was wet and matted like a cloth, like a dog when it gets wet. At first they thought it was dead. It had the shapelessness of meat.

The boy saw it lain in the short grass by the bank, by the dry droppings and the scuff marks of other rabbits and the thick hard blackthorn above, coming into fruit.

"Hey, look," said the boy. He didn't want his brother to see it, but he knew now the other boy would see it anyway so he said it.

The other boy stood away from the rabbit for a moment then edged to it and peered over it and neither of them were sad because the rabbit was dead.

The eyes were open and they did not move. Around them the breeze was going warmly through the blackthorn and the ticking sound of a tractor working came to them across the fields. Then the rabbit's eye moved.

The smaller boy went to prod it with his toe because he needed to understand better. He screwed up his face when he stretched out his foot. The eye moved slowly, just half-closing but not quite: as if it were willing itself just to close.

"Don't prod it, it's still alive," said the other boy. The tractor ticked and chugged far away. They were both of them sad then but they did not want the other to see it. They stood around and nearly walked off and they knew it wasn't a right thing.

"I'm going to finish it off," said the older boy. It was simple and brave, what he said.

When he said it the rabbit kicked but could not get up so it just combed round in a half-circle and it was like the rabbit was helping the boy to do what he said. Like it was trying to tell him with his desperation that it was the right thing. And they knew they had to kill the rabbit then because it was dying.

They looked around and there were some old stones by a wall and the younger boy picked up the biggest stone he could in both hands and looked at the older boy bravely because he was hurt when he saw the rabbit kicking and was confused and would do it himself.

The younger boy loved the older boy and would do it because of the way the older boy had said so quietly and straight that it had to be done and he knew that the older boy felt very sad inside, perhaps sadder than him.

"It might not die properly," said the older boy. "I'll try and not hurt it and just do it quick." It made the younger boy feel sick when he knew he didn't have to kill the rabbit. The older boy picked up one or two stones and they didn't feel right and then he found one which sat in his hand and thought it would be okay. The stone was warm and flat in the older boy's hand.

He always told the younger boy to do the things he didn't want to but this time he didn't; so the younger boy knew it was a very big thing they were doing.

The rabbit was twisted and all the wrong shape since trying to move and the boy knelt down close by it. He didn't want to touch the rabbit with his hands.

"Don't touch it with your hands," he said, "because it might be poisoned and we can't wash our hands." He wanted to touch the rabbit with his hands so he could calm it so it could die gently.

He'd heard about this disease; how his mother's brothers when they were younger would have to go out around the farmland and would come back with bags full of rabbits that they had shot. They had to burn them. And he knew that the disease still happened, but not so bad.

He put his foot on the rabbit's shoulder to hold it down where he thought he should hit it on the neck and the rabbit's deep and sad eye opened at him and was deep and very beautiful. And the boy didn't show anything but inside he asked the rabbit if it was all right to do this and the rabbit's eye just half-closed in defeat, very slowly. He hit the rabbit with the edge of the stone. He hit it as hard as he thought but he couldn't bring himself to want to hurt the rabbit, which was necessary, so the rabbit jerked under his foot and its back legs stretched and kicked. He hit it again in the neck where he had hit it before and there was a lot of muscle there and now the mouth was open and the tiny teeth showed, and the eye looked at him black and flashing with fear. Then he knew he had to hurt the rabbit and in him was the horrible slow panic of knowing something like this. He put the edge of the stone hard into the neck and just pushed and turned and tried to crush.

He wanted the rabbit to die very much now and there was a click and the eye flashed and he knew it was done. The tiny mouth was gritted with strain and the teeth looked very sharp and white.

The younger boy was holding the big rock in both his hands up by his cheek and when he saw from his brother's face that it was done he dropped it away and it landed on the dry ground with a deep thud.

They didn't feel good about the rabbit dying but it was better. They took some old concrete from around the dry wall and took it over to the rabbit. When they went back to the rabbit it looked quiet and peaceful. The younger boy felt sorry for his brother and looked at him to see if he was okay and he was. The older boy told him about how another thing might take the rabbit and then take the poison; so they covered it up with the pads of concrete. The younger boy put the concrete over the rabbit's head and wanted to walk away very quickly because his hand, for a moment, had brushed the fur; the older boy put the cement down on the rest of the rabbit and it wouldn't balance so he turned it over and rested it down. When he rested it down, the back leg moved.

When they walked away he did not tell the younger boy that the back leg had moved and told himself a lot that things moved after they were dead for a while because the nerves jumped. He'd seen his father skin an eel and even without a head it had jumped and twitched. He wished that he knew he'd killed the rabbit. He did not tell the younger boy that the back leg had moved because he knew that this knowing—the rabbit not dead perhaps and dying still under the heavy concrete—was only his; and he thought: "if I had touched it with my hands I would have known for sure." He knew then that people must be very strong.

The breeze was up a little and it was nice because it had been dry for so long, and still; and the two boys left the track and walked quickly over the low, green field, and the younger boy rubbed his hand where it had touched the rabbit's fur.

NINA BOGIN

The White Month

1   WINTER

Quarter moons and half-moons,
waxing and waning through bitter skies.
Snowfall. Thaw. Frost. Rain.
Arrows of sunlight through charcoal clouds.
Sundown's fuchsia flames.
Twilight. Night. Hidden stars.
Silent dawns. Gentle rustlings of birds.
O wake and arise.

2   WINDOW

Squirreled indoors, peeling off
the paper-thin leaves of Brussels sprouts
with the old paring knife. Scent of green.
Faint sunlight at the kitchen window.
Flurry of feathers as blue tits and finches
skid across the stone table strewn with seeds.

3   SONG

An east wind. Mustard-yellow sunlight
zigzags across trees and hills.
The air is fresh as running water.

High in the branches, magpies chatter.
Blackbirds sit in the hornbeam hedge,
calling out their liquid, hopeful song.
Long is the month of January.
Boundless is the patience of the birds.

4   CROWS

Afternoon hushed and shuttered.
Snow-light. Crows caw from one
tree-top to another. They're always
at the ready, flying off in twos
or threes, dropping down
on different branches to converse
and complain. With all their fuss
and natter, who takes any
notice of them now, like the boy
who cried wolf, the girl
who claimed the house was on fire?

5   CHORES

Lavender-scented laundry
to hang up to dry.
Airing of bedclothes

by the open window.
Plumping of pillows,
straightening of sheets.
Vacuuming in and out
of the rooms,
stirring up a storm.
Whisk of the broom
through the kitchen,
in the corners,
behind the doors.
Mopping of the floors.
Dust-shake.
Sponge-swipe.
Carrots to scrub.
Onions to slice.
Water to bring to a boil.
Tasks, chores,
the ordinary toil
that takes us
by the scruff of the neck,
squares our shoulders,
sets us straight.
How else
would the job get done?
Step by step.
Rung after rung.
I cannot live on words alone.

6   FRUGAL

Frugal are the days
of January
doling out
their sober light
on flattened grass,
dull-brown hills.
We lie low,
assailed
by dark visions.
But now the snow
glides in
with a light
of its own,
swan-white,
effortless,
falling
as if it had all
the time in the world,
and stillness
to heal
the most fretful
of souls.

7 HOUSES

Crystal-sharp air over
fallen snow. Spice-scent
of wood smoke. We walk
along the brook. Snowflakes
drift down from the north,
from the west. The everyday
houses are softened, as if
at last they could bring comfort
to the people who live there.

8 TRACKS

Trees sink down under snow.
The day draws out
into paler blue, wisps of grey.
Tracks crisscross the meadow,
intersect, run parallel—
deer, fox, mouse, squirrel,
birds of every feather,
cats from all the houses.
And who can say
those staggered imprints
emerging from the hedge
are not the tracks
of the hare we'll never see
who, alert to every danger,

quivering with fear,
musters its courage
and boldly leaps
across the snow at night
when we are fast asleep?

9   THAW

Sunlight warms us at midday.
Through the melting snow,
patches of grass spread out
like the maps of a new country
with rivers and meadows,
lowlands and wetlands,
estuaries opening out to the sea…
But the world is old, old,
and ailing. It waits for us
as it has always waited.
And we are too late.

GRO DAHLE

TRANSLATED BY REBECCA WADLINGER

The Dust, The Shadow, The Dog, and Me

1

Is it I who listens?
Is it I who stops?
Waits?
Is it the wind I hear?
Is it the water?

An open space, a sea,
someone screaming?
Is it I who falls?
Or do I continue on?

I look at the woods behind the house
the dark wall of trees.
But the forest has no words,
not for this.

2

A catastrophe comes into the house
without making an appointment, without knocking.
Suddenly it is here
and takes all the space,
continues to grow,
bursts the day into bits, the world into pieces,

paints the walls dark,
nails up crosses.

3

It is not possible to know about
a catastrophe in advance.
Look, there he comes up the road.
Point him out.
In five years this is going to happen.

A passing glance,
a crossing train.

My hands look like ordinary hands,
but I do not know what they can do.
I do not know what my mouth can find to say.
What if I have been wrong the whole time,
that I lead myself deeper and deeper?

The nettles still rustle,
the ferns still tangle their leaves,
They do not change,
they stay where they always stay,
hold the world steady
with their roots.

4

Sometimes the world goes to pieces.
The sun continues to shine.
The dog still sits on the stairs.
The light falls differently on the road.
It is another light, another road.
The road goes to another place,
but I do not know where.

The shift is already underway.
Movement has changed direction,
I no longer know where my feet are going.
Gravity pulls toward another point.
I no longer know who I am.
My name is blown away.

5

Is it me
or the trees
who cry
early in the morning?

It must be the trees.
It is they who sigh.

Their tears
lie in the grass and glitter.

It must be the trees
spreading rumors
with the wind.
Who else would it be?
The magpies?

It is not true
what they say.
Do not listen to what they say about me.

MALCOLM BARRETT

Tanka Book

TANKA 1: BENEATH

My dad with the snake
Wriggling between his palms.
My brother's eyes sharp.

Who knows how many of us
Will dig up our hidden guns?

TANKA 2: THE BUFFALO

My brother sobbing
Asking where our father is,
Beer-smell on is breath.

Countless times over, Black Elk
Has licked that steaming liver.

TANKA 3: IN YOUR OWN HOME

Cleaning your wet tail,
I set my mala on you.
What else could I do?

Nanapush, it's not so bad,
All the work under this roof.

TANKA 4: FOR JANET

This inheritance,
Like the ground beneath our feet,
Opens up the way.

Don't take it too personally
If it's strange in the moonlight.

TANKA 5: WINTER

I remember the
Blue vein of your white arm as
I tried to talk you
Through to the other side. I'll
never think you understood.

TANKA 6: FLAGPOLE

Waiting for the cops
In the cold Florida sand,
Can you come back now?

Under my arm, you are gone,
Stuck in the earth like a pole.

TANKA 7: NO ROBINS IN BROOKLYN

There aren't any robins here.
Could there be some tiny bones
Somewhere in this nest?

On my way to buy heat pads,
The clouds won't cover the moon.

TANKA 8: TREASURY

Tikka wakes me up
By licking my left eyelid,
Tongue like a pumice stone.

The fields flood. Nobody minds
When the cat goes back to sleep.

TANKA 9: WHITE ONION

A white onion fell
Between my robe and me. It
Split us like an axe.

But grandma kept one in bed
To get rid of her back pain.

TANKA 10: ON THE LINE

A daddy longlegs
Walked slowly through the zendo.
It offered itself
To the zabuton's shadow,
Smoking like an altar box.

TANKA 11: ECHO ROCK

You say I am too
Close to the edge of the cliff.
You're right. Still, I stay.

Like mist, two hundred feet down,
Porcupines sleep in wet trees.

TANKA 12: WHAT I TRY TO BE WHEN OFFERING INCENSE IN THE MORNING

Like the man covered
In warts that suddenly all
Fall off at once.

Like the White Dragon, sipping
water from the altar cup.

TANKA 13: BY YOUR GRAVE

Sometimes I play the
Lottery so I can lose
Like you used to do.
Now, there's a whole continent
On top of you, beneath me.

Empty Field 1: Bright, Boundless Field

We're just fine by the
Fish markets, ten minutes from
Those places to drown.

It's bright under this spire
And there's no beet field in sight.

Our coffees are small.
I'd like to say something brave—
Maybe something like,

"I'd gladly give my kidney
To the god of doors and gates."

I suppose there are
Some pros and cons to being
Cracked open like crabs.

It's honest—but, in the end,
Whom does it go on to feed?

No Title

Maybe it's true that I'm more like a cave of snow.

You know the type. Brought up the boy in the afternoon & gone
by evening.

Listen, will you lick the snow off my boot? It's what my cat
used to do.

No, it's OK. It's too much to ask. It's like a muskrat lifting its
head at dusk.

The water parts & suddenly you've got a million years of
heritage & dinner for Lent.

The tracks are frozen & all I've got is this coffee & a book on
biostatistics.

Worse yet, I don't know how much luck you'd have calling
these wet streets snow.

ARIELLE GREENBERG

A Way Out

I want to take a vow of chastity: to write only toward what I don't know

If I come to know something, I should allow it to be divine and not
    speak of it

A dream while in Maine of seeing huge clouds made of millions of small
    stones
gathering and hovering above the ocean at the horizon, moving toward
    shore

An inevitable apocalypse we are powerless to stop, can only see coming

Also some sense of this being what I think foolishly that I can escape:
    clusters of black doom

In the dream it seems both inescapable and that I have indeed found a
    way out

Have I found a way out

Door made of stones, door in the stone wall

My mind is the black box that contains the ticker tape key to my
    dissatisfaction
The recording of my unease

All at once I feel the stone wall in my stomach
To place by hand, round by round, the sense of it I never had

The reason for a story of a dam in any culture

A house does not make a person happy
But a house can be a quiet place with wood smoke and side
    porch and raised vegetable bed
Where there is the effort made to be your happy self
Maybe

Woodland Valley Waldorf Fair

Like the bar game—nestle a shaker in its salt, then blow and
see if it still stands—I lose my daughter in a storm in a dream.
We're at a woodland valley Waldorf fair, all felted contentment,
and the next minute she's racing up the stone steps toward the
road, and me caught in the crowd with the baby can't get to her
quite, and am calling and calling when the thunder claps and all
the stone goes slick.

  I'm trying to do too much, the salt says. I will lose or slip or
topple. Keep the kids close now, the dark cloud says. The hill is
steep, the street trafficked at the top, and the climb worse when
it's wet.

Pastoral: Uncoupling

If I could go back and unmarry you,
mark my commitments only in metals and gems and ink,
children and kitchens and gardens but no government—

I bought three etched glass tumblers—

Where there was a pair, now a trinity, now a _____.
Where there was an apple, now a pear, and a berry bush
    budding—

Come what may—

So I shall scatter my lights—

And if you are not my domesticated only, my fait accompli?
More and more and more—

JOSEFINE KLOUGART

TRANSLATED BY MARTIN AITKEN

One of Us Is Sleeping

I wake up. The room is no longer cold, but the bed is clammy and damp. It keeps hold of its dankness. The room faces out back and is used only when we girls are home, seldom now.

My younger sister is always busy, we all are.

A rush and bustle handed down through generations. Sit down here awhile. Work unfinished. The cold of the sheets and admonishment. I don't really know what it is to feel welcome. I know what it is to belong. Except then I become unsure.

I feel, though with a delay.

Always ahead.

I meet you and immediately I see everything. A pair of scissors catching just right on a length of cloth, the blade finding its direction through the texture that is the fabric skeleton; the cloth opens and is a fruit whose flesh is white. Such moments I live for, though never discover until later. Like when you sit there thinking it's too late, now, to think of whether to stay a second longer.

What if you stayed too long.

What if you stayed forever and never went farther away than that you could responsibly allow yourself to take a taxi home.

When such things happen, thoughts that arrive too late, they consume you and refuse to let go of your pale body, my pale body—trembling with something like doubt. I know nothing, and yet I have seen everything. The realization that resides in that; that there are eyes that *see*, and eyes that do not *know*.

A wish to be recognized as the person you are, to find such eyes, a human gaze.

Cross-eyed days in which you hope. Most days are like that, most eyes.

I am tired and wish to see clearly, a gaze that is knives and scissors, an incision into what really is. That's how I want to see, and how I want to be seen. It'll be a mess, a filthy mess. Disorder everywhere, disappointment as far as the eye can see. But you. And me, who sees you. Maybe it's more than enough, maybe it's all you can ask for.

WINTER. THE SNOW RUMBLING IN STILL, WITHOUT sound. Sometime after Christmas, I'm not sure.

The snow. That has laid itself upon it all, all that dares to remain exposed for more than a few seconds at a time, upon everything dead and everything living; the living and the dead; the violet stalks of the Brussels sprouts all askew, keeping their balance in the broken rows of the vegetable garden, packed in by snow, as old wine bottles are encapsulated by melting, then stiffening candle wax, and the snow falls with the drowsy resolve of that image.

Obstinacy all around. We can't go anywhere. We are inside a house, and the house is a giant corpse. We lie here and wait, beneath the skin. Movements are agitated and take place indoors. Outside only when something compels one of us: to fetch wood for the fire, feed the birds, clear a path. Outside there is only snow and the flies. True, the fattest of the flies are survivors.

The roasting trays are by turn hot and cold. We girls stand and stare, crane our necks beneath the ceilings. Fledgling birds. Our mother, nearly burning the bread. It can still be done, in the old oven. Her lips tighten and she winces at the sizzle of wet cloth, the only thing she has time to put between her fingers and the hot tray. She burns herself, the skin blisters: the things I do for you, she says, a wry smile. The water runs from the tap, I am horrified. The two sisters each understand more or less than me, who understands exactly what is required to see the fatality of it, in that sentence. Blisters.

Nothing to be worried about, she says, comforting me, in that way. She means it, and yet her words are a weight to haul back into the boat, the clothes of the men are heavy with water, and we must sail on. Once more an about-turn; we always comforted each other *in reverse*; when I need comfort, when she does.

I think I looked utterly distraught.

The warm filling runs out of the sweet Shrovetide buns. The recipe book lies open on the table, *Karolines Køkken*. The filling of the buns, vanilla, and these rich yolks. I spell out the words on the title page, the Dairy Association's recipe series, the oddness of the subtitle, *Oh, Freedom*—someone must have been thinking of heaven, or something quite like it.

Sunday mornings at the Thorup Dairy. My eyes watering at the muslin cheesecloths, the dairymen slicing the blocks with wires. You can work in the dairy when you grow up, my father says to me. Perhaps that's where it comes from: the idea of your parents, for all that, not knowing you better. The disappointment of them not seeing the gravity of it. He hands me a slice of cheese, draped over his fingers, and I remember thinking of dog ears, the same feeling of body about it.

I hated the smell of sour milk, the swarming cheese. An army of holes. And I wanted to go in and yet not for anything in the world, to go in. The wind from the sea across the road sweeps across the parking spaces and me, a mad dog thrashing in its chains, I shake my hair and drag a comb of fingers across its ribs before clambering into the rear seat.

The bread has risen immensely, its back split open like a wound. The bread, the comb of its broken spine.

An old friend she has forgotten and suddenly recalls. My mother. She misses him, repeatedly. I'm not sure.

My lips are cracked. My thoughts.

My mother ties our hands behind our backs with her eyes, goes from the oven without closing it first; the oven issuing its heat into the kitchen. We try *not* to look each other in the eye. We glance about the room, our eyes are darts whizzing about the bread and the leaking filling of the Shrovetide buns as it sizzles on the tongue's metal.

The mother returns to her young in the kitchen again, interrupting them with her example: look, my wounded hands, she says. Holding them out in front of her. So that her offspring may inspect. The fledglings gather on the finger branches. They nod.

The tips of her fingers are swathed in band-aids. Ten little brown boxes on skin-covered bones. Their mother's hands, at least one joint in excess, as with each of her arms, each of her legs, shins, lower arms. And her bottom lip is twice as big, she has doubled in size.

Her hair is thick and glossy, wet slabs of molded blue clay. Her beaded bracelets rattle as her young once more look away. She is melancholy for three days, then busy for three, but her love is the same every day, quite insane and far more durable than anything ever before seen in this world. Her *remaining*. Something rare in that, that choice: remaining until—

Until what, exactly. Until the end. Until it no longer makes sense, until she is abandoned by us or by our father or by the feeling that in spite of everything there is meaning in the madness, the victims.

She puts bread and sweet buns in the freezer for the birthdays in spring. Her children were born in March, April, and May. If she's to be believed.

Sometimes I'm not sure, she can be so *absorbed*.

There is a fundamental lack of credibility about busy people, the way they insist on besieging dates and days and half-nights, annexing the world like that, colonially, with their own bodies. Come home for Christmas. Come home in good time.

Later, I'm like that myself, it's what all of us grow up to be, all three of us, in part, at least. At best there's something naïvely mendacious about that kind of vigor. At worst it's calculation, thinly veiled. So many important dates. So many children and even more mouths to feed and navels from which to pick the fluff. Giddyap, giddyap, all my horses!

Always this wish to be just as busy. Just as decent as our mother; we are watermarked. Maybe one day just like her, without these grubby, rural fingernails.

But our cuticles resist. My nails collect dirt. Earth is what they want.

I bring in some wood, a bustle of activity. A few seconds is all, and then a pillar of salt.

THE GOLD-THREADED BRISTLES OF A CARCASS POKE up windswept, to be tumbled over the cloak of snow. So coarse, encapsulated each by frost, and the ice cap's desolate.

A slothful movement in the snow. Most things have given up and lie still. A slightness of motion every ten seconds. The world is giving a ball, and at each round an animal is selected, or a tree, or a person, who must leave the stage and retire to the wings with ears blushing. The ones who didn't move. Wrapped in hide of bison. The birds are in panic. No leaves remain to return the sound of their beating wings. No socks hung out to dry on the line, the metal hearts of the clothespins are glazed with pristine ice, frost blooms by turn on blue and red plastic. Posing arms of crystal. There is nothing like the echo of a world such as this.

I wake up with a snap, its beginnings a hesitation some hours after midnight. The wind switching to the east. The movement is an exact reflection of the slip of continental plates during an earthquake. Blankets of snow avalanching by turn. A shroud of matted marrow for the outer layer of the snow-cloak.

The sigh of the curly kale, its shelves of leafage.

Blankets that drop from plant cots.

An audible crashing-down. The smell of something giving way. Something else sinking slightly.

Crystal arms colluding with panes of glass, and something contracts and gathers in a droplet. A droplet plunges from the eaves to land upon the sunken head of a withered rose. The nod of the bush. My pillow has grown into my brain. She, who is used to stained and lumpy pillows, will fall asleep with her head in most any bony lap.

This infernal sound of droplets impacting and disintegrating. I wake up more fatigued than when I lay down to sleep.

ON THE LAST DAY OF THE YEAR, my mother claps her hands in front of her chest, her eyes become tender mussels, orbs wedged tightly between lips of calcium. She enthuses—a rush of sibilants—about the grapes, Léon Millot, the ones she cuts in bunches from the vine in the greenhouse.

Being able to do such a thing. In December.

Winter all around. If this is not a miracle; if this is a miracle.

THAT WAS HOW I IMAGINED IT. THAT was what I wanted, to return here and to have a family of my own, in the village where we lived. The kind of face you see as you turn your head quickly inside an old house at evening, houses with such *sounds*.

There are images that will always occupy me. I have come to see them again, to be done with them again, or rather not, to not be done with them, ever. To continue being occupied. Continue *staying*, and yet leave.

YOU ARE PEELING AN ONION, YOU STRIKE it hard against the chopping board and remove the outer layers with a large knife. Out in the yard they are slaughtering chickens. They ask me to fetch more boiling water in which to scald them, or polystyrene boxes to divide things up. A cow, half a cow. I vomit over the fence, into the pasture of sheep, my bile dangling like entrails in the windowed rectangles of wire, where it remains for some time before descending into the couch grass. Take her inside, someone says, and my mother smiles and comforts me. The onions, tenderizing in the pot. I find myself thinking you look like my father. You look like my father, I whisper. In the darkness you turn, sedated by fatigue.

What.

You look like my father, I say again.

They roll back to sleep. The kitchen sparkles, stars illuminate the bedroom. Can a room be dark and then so abruptly light without anyone having altered anything. The same stars in the sky, the same night.

You sigh; later, a whimper. To what kind of exile have you delivered me, your sleeping, sleeping body wonders, a wheezing enquiry.

What do you think. What do you want. But at the same time, I regret everything, approached by creeping nausea, the kind that reminds a person they knew all along and even savored the disaster's unfolding. I have a penchant for catastrophe. There is comfort in the sun always going down. The fact that in a way there is no hope, you know it is what will happen, and we can do nothing to prevent it. Death. I pick up a couple of blankets from the lawn, the dew has fallen, I tell myself, and again I am doing this too late (this is the kind of thing that makes me doubt I am no longer a child, and wonder if I will ever be anything else).

We drive through the plantation to Svinklovene. The roads are uneven concrete, massive slabs split like clay plowed up and frozen overnight, in the first frost. Lie down here. And the covering of morning: the world hushed, only the rhythmic snap of the flaglines, pealing bells in the distance; and then we are at the harbor, some buckets put down in a basement somewhere,

where washing machines idle—outside, everything is silent, like an odd shoe someone lost on the road.

Your body is accusatory, because I have taken you with me. That is your dream.

And yet you have no dream other than peace, so why blame me. Simple.

I SUPPOSE I HAD GROWN USED TO you, your being here; the sound of my own heart, the sound of a bush beating at the window all night, all day.

IT'S RAINING, AS IF THERE WERE A fire to put out, a steady downpour throughout the day, a recalcitrant blaze that will not succumb. When was rain ever a solution to anything.

The flies are busy. They scurry across the walls of the kitchen, hasten across my sister's hand. She lets the hot water run in the sink, on the empty bottles with their stoppers.

Her hand, a surface of skin gripped by flies, is at rest on the counter.

DISTANCE HAS SHORTENED EVERYWHERE, NO LONGER AS far from one place to another since they cleared the trees. I go left, down through the wood that is no more. I think of you, decide to call you, but then to wait until later. That feeling I have: of always holding you off. I wonder whether the sentence can be inverted: if you have always held me off. And I—whether I took something in advance that ended up being canceled. I follow the stream, through the snow. I can't be on my own anymore, and I've only just started. It has nothing to do with strength, or lack of strength. It's about what makes sense. A friend writes me a letter, on this day of all days, he writes that you can't love a person who *cannot* love. I know he's thinking: because it ruins you. I'm not sure who I'm thinking about. Dead man. New man.

One kind of gravity colliding with another, that's what it is. Being home, and being nowhere at all. Being somewhere you know, without recognizing a thing. I walk the path into the woods. The hills are older, the woodland has advanced all the way up to the vertex; bald, sandy earth.

Does it mean anything, me walking here.

Maybe it means: you are walking here. No more than that. I want to call you, but I want never to call you again. The feeling that wells in me is of a celebration canceled. A number of people want to love me but are not allowed. A number of people cannot, or lack the courage. It doesn't matter. All there is here is this acute lack of home. The trees are bare, oak, I think. Yes, oak. A low carpet of self-seeded evergreen advancing to the trunks. They look frightened, as though, being caught red-handed on the point of some shameless deed, they lost their crowns in panic. You use me for thinking. I don't know what use I make of you, apart perhaps from survival. There is no one in the twilight here to notice that the trees and their crowns don't match. Evergreen and deciduous are different. And still I don't doubt that is what has happened: panic arisen among the trees, and sudden autumn. Leaf fall, a carpet of needles around the lower trunks, the feet of the oak.

BECAUSE LANGUAGE IS NOT INNOCENT, BUT FIRE and weaponry. One wages war with words, risking all the time to fall into bed with the enemy. I'm not sure now, but that's what I thought when I got up and saw a boat come though the canal, towing the morning behind it on a rope. I'm not sure either if there is any pleasure in not being *compelled* to do something. And more generally: pleasure surely has little to do with such a thing as freedom.

I GET OUT OF BED AND STAND naked in the blue light. My feet seem unnaturally flat. It's like the original and the acquired have changed places. My heeled sandals missing, the soles of my feet are admitted to the floors.

THE APPLE TREE RUNS IN THROUGH THE window and along the hall. Its branches are trailing flames. The apples bruise against the walls.

The storm has woken me up.

The different sounds of the apples. The frozen red ones. Those succumbing, those rotten.

Branches swipe at furniture, stab at the pictures. The blue lithographs sway like street lamps, they buffet the wall, in the way of unknowing birds whose wings have been clipped. Helpless and inept.

If I can't identify the moments I live for, at least I can identify those I live in spite of.

Nature is disturbed by winter. I am, too.

I ASK IF WE CAN EAT IN the kitchen. The darkness is too oppressive here. My face is warm with sleep that never became sleep. A long day. An exhaustion that comes of the day. My father arriving home, his footsteps through the living room, to the piano. I hear him put down his car keys, see them reflect for a moment in the black varnished wood.

And then they are still and silent in their place. The lake gapes beneath the ice, but the winter is a lid on top of all that is living, all that is dead: as the snow that falls, all the living and all the dead.

Do you remember, I say quietly, when we found that big fish in the lake.

My mother looks up. She is standing with a teaspoon in her hand, removing pips from a cucumber, scraping one half, then the other. She has a steady hand. The same with fish, the way she removes the bones in a single movement, with ease.

I think so, she says. Last winter, was it. Or the one before. It must have been the one before.

It was trapped in the ice, I say. And my hands have come to a halt; my eyes notice them, the way they have come to rest on the chopping board.

I am not breathing.

We both know it must be the winter before last, because last winter we couldn't see each other. I had *made a choice*, she said. After that she fell ill, then presumably forgot her disappointment; color washes from wood if only it is left long enough in the sea. It doesn't disappear, but becomes like the winter: only lighter. Increasingly iridescent, a price on my head that continues to rise. A competition in which we have forgotten to time ourselves.

It must have been, I say. Last year. Why hasn't he said hello, I ask.

She raises her eyebrows and looks so sad all of a sudden.

Perhaps he's, I don't know…

She turns the cucumbers on the chopping board, slices them into staves, dices them, then lifts the board over to a bowl of yogurt, sweeping it clean with the spine of the blade.

Tired, I suggest.

Tired, yes. That'll be it.

I crush three cloves of garlic and peel them, passing them on to her with the garlic press. I put the dry skins in the trash. Hi, Dad, I call into the living room. He has sat down at the piano. It needs tuning, always some note that resists. He plays as if there's something important he wishes to announce to someone.

What is it about that fish.

I don't know why. I just started thinking about it.

It did look so very strange. Caught in the ice, and frozen solid.

I nod. It's funny, but it suddenly feels like—well, a long time ago.

It is, she says. Rinsing the chopping board and wiping it dry. I suppose he must be, tired.

He gives me a kiss on the cheek. Do you want red wine, he asks. Yes, I say to please him. Or to comfort myself. That's probably it. I drink three glasses while we eat. They open another bottle. Should we open another bottle. Yes, why not.

What are you doing, she asks me as we brush our teeth before bed. That won't help. I shrug. I shouldn't have come.

Of course you should. The way you're feeling.

I shrug again. I think there's something fine about repeating it all the time.

YOU'RE NOT SLEEPING.

No, I'm not sleeping. My mother sits down on the sofa opposite. She gets up again almost in the same movement, places a log in the wood stove. Opens the flue. The influx of air sucks flames from the embers.

She sits down again and draws a blanket over her. It's impossible to tell what she wants. I am lying on the made-up sofa, the rear cushions heaped in a pile at the end.

I don't know why you won't sleep upstairs. The bed's made up and the heat's on.

The fire, I say. It's nice to lie here and look at the fire.

She nods, watching it with me, staring into the flames. We both think of my grandmother, the time she lay here, the last winter she was alive. I know exactly that it is what my mother is thinking about. The way her own mother was unable to reconcile herself with the glass window of the stove, the way she kept calling for us to tell us this: the house is on fire.

There's *meant* to be fire, we said, it's a stove for heating. It stays inside, nothing will happen.

Why didn't we just move her into the office, I ask out of the blue.

My mother shrugs. That's where I get it from, I think to myself. My shoulders are an echo of my mother's.

She was afraid in the night, I think. How could we let her lie like that, I ask into the room. Afraid in the night.

She slept eventually, my mother says, defensively.

Perhaps, I say. Or maybe her face grew tired. My fingers feel my own face, as though to see for themselves. Was it tired of looking sad. Was there any clarification. There was no way of telling.

Who is it you're grieving over anyway, she suddenly asks.

I am not even surprised by her question.

I don't know, I say calmly. Have you noticed the apple tree, I ask.

The fire settles. The wind has died, it calms the flame.

Which one, she asks. She draws a cushion under her head and makes herself comfortable.

I can't help thinking about her body underneath the blanket. Like the plaster cast of a body.

Mine, I say quietly.

Have you got your *own* apple tree, she asks. Which one is it.

Don't you remember, that afternoon. We were each given a tree. It was your idea. I chose first, I don't even think the others were that interested. I don't think they cared.

Oh, says my mother. I do remember now, faintly. The low tree, the one you can see from the bedroom.

Yes, that's the one, I nod.

My mother's legs, her blue chest. You can see the movements of her heart inside her chest.

I'm not sure I know who you're grieving over.

No, I say. How could you, when I don't even know myself. Have you noticed the tree, it's still got apples on it.

Has it. That's good for the birds.

What sort are they. They're red. And very dark. Not Ingrid Marie, I'd recognize those.

I turn onto my back and look through the room. The joists slice it apart. When can you take sprigs in, I ask. Will they blossom if you take them in now.

I don't think so. They need buds first. In March you should be able to. Then they'll flower. She talks about the spring, March, April, May. I'm not listening. I'm already asleep.

ROWAN RICARDO PHILLIPS

Étude on Man

How easy life made it to turn the words
Into a man. Blind-sugar being: man.
I took the five hooks from my mouth and said:
Be a man; justify the ways of God
To man; oh, man; etc. Maybe when I say
A man I really mean you or my mom
Or the blankness of blank verse blanking out
A name, likely some loose version of you
Or my mom but certainly not all this,
Which happens later. Disinterest in you
Grew. Man's mansong grew. Thus we related,
Erring. A cock in the hand was a red
Herring. Reading bore Stevens, Updike, Swift,
And Keith Haring, but none of them voted
In the last election. My mind's not right.
I'll leave now. It's like stepping back from a
Shattered mirror. And then seeing it heal.

Hart and Abercromby Étude

The Old Fire Station Conference Center
Near Woodford Square in downtown Port of Spain
Is lightly decorated inside by ten
Chinese lanterns swaying in the AC;
They dangle down from the ceiling's chipped slats.
I have absolutely no idea if
This answers your question. I'm where the streets
Hart and Abercromby meet. And love of
This, in its supreme and singular is,
Its texture instead of its facts, its feel,
Instead of what _____ finds when _____ googles,
The soul in the la of its is, the real.
You ask as though you don't know what it is,
The real, and everything becomes ISIS.

Orpheus, Roaming

Love, it's cold and you're underdressed,
Eat desserts, you'll be ok.

"bad food." If you eat deserts for a whole week…
you'll be ok kissing emoji

Love, it's cold and you're underdressed,
Eat desserts, you'll be ok.

You're far away and by yourself, it's ok.

You don't eat meat and other "bad food."
If you eat deserts for a whole week … you'll be ok kissing emoji

I have to say that it looks really tasty heart-eyed emoji

You're far away and by yourself, it's ok.
You don't eat meat and other

The Question

When did you know you wanted to become
A poet? No one believes this question.
No one listens for the answer. It's one
Of those habits of people forced to live
Together on a spinning rock, the pale
Blue dot a wince in the wide attention
The dying light seeks out from ice giants,
Dull and firm in the dark, under polite
Lights, midst rows and rows of people who ask
When and why about poetry, of she
Who forgets to ask something that was,
I realize later, part of the poem,
The part where it all comes together and,
Having come together, finally sings.

JULIA THACKER

A Guide for Caregivers

January 7, 1945. The sky
over the Rhine is lush with violet smoke.
There is the metallic smell of blood and sulfur,
a field jacket stationed inside
the cedar-lined chiffarobe.
The tapioca has been tampered with.

In the warehouse of antique fathers
don't indulge in baby talk. Call things
by their names: *salt, fork, mercy, butter*.

To him, loner, hoarder
of aluminum TV dinner trays,
luster after telephone books
dating back to 1961,
collector of wheat pennies, extinguisher
of a son's spirit,

answer questions simply but clearly.
    I am your daughter.
    I am a teacher.
    I have no children.
    I am not acquainted with anyone named Goddamned
        Glorie.
    I live on the Atlantic Coast hundreds of miles away.
    You cannot leave with me.

Allow yourself to be introduced as a sister,
a stranger, the aforementioned
Glorie. If you are addressed
by the names of the dead—Edna Ruth, Anna Lenore—
rise and offer your hand.

Honor the soliloquy of gibberish.
On the topic of hallucinations:
when there is a loquacious tale of driving to Tallahassee
yesterday to take in a baseball game,
how the redhead was mad (*She stomped out of the ballpark*),
tell him you are glad he had the chance to get away,
Florida is lovely this time of year.

When he confides that it was Corporal X
who pinned the paper target over the heart of
the German spy trussed
and lashed to the stake, express interest.

If his only other visitor
is a holiness preacher, call these garbled words
divine. Reminisce about the ramshackle
pinewood church in the hollows
of Appalachia, speaking in tongues,
snake handling, foot-washing.
When the minister says

even the rich will enter Heaven barefoot,
offer your godless assent,
for your old one is already washed by strangers,
his ass wiped, naked as the moon.

These instructions are directed particularly
to daughters in late middle-age
who pass back and forth in the halls of the memory-care
unit, the bucolic Spring Cottage
at Spring Hills Singing Woods.
The daughters, their necks crepey under floral scarves,
stylishly acquainted with oblivion,
embarrassed to still be someone's child,
who purchase expensive fish oils to aid recollection
and stand before mirrors in the rooms of chain motels
reciting the names of famous rivers, chanting
times tables.

Above all, no trading of fathers.
Do not take the hand of the retired history teacher
with the snazzy button-down
and honeyed voice.
Do not lead him to his room and straighten
family pictures on the walls or fold
the afghan on back of his recliner.
Do not think, *Who would know?*
It is too late to go shopping for fathers.

When you take leave of your ancient one
do not speak of the future.
Do not say, Tomorrow we will plant the foggy trees.
Do not say, Dad, we are not in Belgium,
we're in Dayton, Ohio,
on the Midwestern plain of industrial farms
where cattle are pumped full of drugs, corralled,
fattened, felled, and shipped
by rail. We are in the great Midwest
and the downtowns are empty
as though there had been a great war.

Do not recite the names of the drugs on his chart,
however beautiful: Zoloft, Depakote Sprinkles.
Do not say, Father, I am like you, psycho-
tropic. Do not mention the bottle
of Xanax in your carry-on.
Do not say, There is thunder inside our blue raincoats.
Soon we will explode like stars.
The skies will open. Our sleeves
will be empty and full of wind.
Our cells like constellations are replicating
every day with errors.

Dear Earth

Please excuse my father's tardiness as his soul has a slight fever.
It has been snowing here for days. The roads have been salted.
Please excuse. There has been an electrical storm in his mind
with shortages and outages and his thoughts are as blank as
a deserted barn. His legs will no longer support his weight,
but his heart, that aubergine thing, with its winded pipes, its
whistles, its ventricles, its secret chambers, will not stop beating.
We console ourselves at the winter farmers' market with scarlet
turnips and a cider of fermented ginger.

Dear Earth, please excuse my father. He has a dental
appointment to have his mouth stuffed with roses. His
body will be shipped to Appalachia per his request. He will
be traveling alone, the casket tagged. He is a solitary. His
preference is to journey by land along the rutted roads and
steep mountain drop-offs. He wishes to be interred alongside
his drunkard father, a dentist, who now can berate him through
eternity. Earth, make a place for him. Lay him down among
the young Confederates whose eyes are cold marbles in the old
daguerreotypes. Let his bones mingle with shale, fragrant peat,
veins of coal. Let them kiss the amber shards of moonshine
bottles and sea-blue Mason jars. There will be no benediction.
Earth, my religion is words, while yours is water and fire. I
wonder about your temperament. You shift and moan in your
sleep.

I hope this finds you well. Today we put on not one but two
horsehair shirts buttoned to the neck for warmth. Here we
abide, and silence is a virtue. I live exceedingly far north of

the Kentucky mountains. One day I will be ash and pearls
of bone scattered along the rocky coast of New England
beside the Algonquins vanquished by a plague of measles,
among the bleached ribs of sperm whales, of barristers and
stuffy transcendentalists. Earth, I am married to a Quaker
who comes home each evening stamping his heavy boots,
eyebrows salted with frost. He has become brotherly. We do
not hate our parents. Once we did. Now our memories are like
muslin curtains in the window, bleached by the winter sun.
My husband loves me. Each night I lie down with him in the
trundle bed.

Dear Earth, I hope this missive reaches you. Otherwise, I will
appoint myself Post Mistress of the Dead Letter Office, mute
bell above the door. I will sort and catalog the wine-stained
envelopes addressed in a foreign tongue, the indecipherable
postcards, the missed connections, the faded pencil traces,
those beautiful pewter shadows. Earth, I want to stuff my
pockets with messages smuggled from prison camps, pages
torn from ledgers, envelopes left to the elements whose cursive
has smudged to watercolor, the twine-wrapped packages of
nineteenth-century pornography in which large-breasted
women in striped stockings pull corsets to their waists, exposing
nipples like roses, and splay their legs on velvet settees. Earth,
I want to tuck into the waistband of my worsted wool skirt
blank sheets from the madhouse, declarations from soldiers
who fell before their letters were posted, the reporters of
weather *It turned cool today. Roxie canned thirty-four quarts of
white mountain ridge runners and seventeen jars of rhubarb*, her
satisfaction boundless. Earth, I want to drink the blue elixir of
fountain pens, the artisanal blackberry ink.

Please excuse my absence as I have had a touch of melancholia.
I will close. For my husband and I are elders among the wild

tattooed children who have become tribal in their beards and flannel shirts. The lenses of my eyes are brittle, so when I look out onto the world it is blurry, impressionistic. I believe this a kind of radiance. Earth, please admit my father. I want it to be over. I want it to end. Perhaps this life is a dream the dead are having. In that case, I write on a tablet of snow and the season is changing. The navy-blue ink runs, smudging the ice-glazed windows. In that case, my words are drowning in the invisible river. I am sincerely yours.

Roma Amor

In late afternoon, when the light
breaks in the shaded tourist cafe,
tired, our faces stripped of glitter and laughter,
the time of day when the dolor
beneath everything is clear as dust,
we don't talk, but listen instead
to the scratchy violin across the courtyard
because it is the instrument
closest to the human voice.
Here, it is alright with me to think
I will die, will lose this one
and that one, and you, though at times,
when the waiter speaks to us, all tone
and scale, in broken English,
we are so close we answer with one voice.
Please bring a plate of sky, a glass of dusk.
It is all right with me to think
I'll be a little inscription on stone
or a cast of light on a field.
My firefly city, Rome,
I bring you my sadness
the way a small town
newspaper lists the weddings and
obituaries on the same page, wedding
forever the dew-faced bride,
the freshly turned black earth,
a handful of rice, a few roses.

ERICA X EISEN

Monday's Child

And I had a black eye once, my brother did me it with a croquet hoop, we were in Phoenix Park and they'd done it all up for Palm Sunday very nice with croquet and lawn bowls and other English things and didn't I win and then my brother nearly blinded me with one of those yokes and Mam gave him a womp on the head like you wouldn't believe, she said Is this how you treat the day of the Lord, and he was crying and I was crying and it was a terrible mess until they gave me my teddy as a prize, who was very smart in a corduroy jumper. Then it wasn't so bad after all.

We go down to the shops on Sunday, to the high street and then into Rita's on the way back, Mam will get the paper for Da and if I was good I can get a sweet. I look all the rows up and down, picking a sweet is a very serious business, there's Rolos and Cadbury Dairy Milks and Mars Bars and Wispas and Fry's Chocolate Creams and Liquorice Allsorts and Polo Mints and Toffee Crisps and Turkish Delights and those queer lavender-tasting ones my nan's always after buying but nobody likes. I tell Mam I want a Terry's Chocolate Orange and she says They're only for Christmas pet and I say Why and she says Keep on like this and you'll have nothing at all so I clamp a hand over my mouth to keep myself from talking and grab a Walnut Whip as quick as you like and Mam takes out her coin purse and says Well now and off we go. Terry's Chocolate Oranges we always get at Christmas and Cadbury Creme Eggs at Easter, only last Easter I got no chocolates on account of I had the German measles and couldn't eat fatty foods and my brother would come into my room and dangle all his sweets in my face and me too weak to do anything about it. Two weeks I was laid up for bed rest, and then the next week I could go down the stairs, I walked down all by myself holding onto the banister, and when I went into the living room my father was reading the evening paper and he looked up and did a big smile and said It's herself.

Singing we always do late at night in pubs. My auntie now isn't she a great one for the Irish songs, "*Mo ghile mear*" and "*Óró sé do bheatha abhaile*" and all them, and Fionn with his "Auld Triangle" and Theresa who studies down at the conservatory in Westland Row does one of those Italian ones that nobody understands but we all clap anyway and say Wasn't she marvelous altogether, and we stand whenever someone sings "The Fields of Athenry." And one time we were down the pub and I did a song my very self, I stood on my chair and I sang "Molly Malone" and everyone joined in for the chorus and when I was done they cheered me and said Good girl except my brother who said Wasn't she a prozzie and my mother gave him a right clobbering and said Diarmuid James O'Leary you are as bold as brass and nobody else said anything except for my auntie who said Sweet suffering Christ.

But that's not true that bit about her being a prozzie, it can't be true or else why would they have a statue of her up in Grafton Street. Anyway the song says she was a fishmonger and that's clear enough, I sometimes think I wouldn't mind being a fishmonger, I love a good piece of fish and I don't mind the smell even, and anyway I could get a song written about me and wouldn't that be grand. The other day I said that, I walked into the living room and said Mam Da I want to be a fishmonger and Mam who was darning my socks said That's nice and Da said Have you done your maths. I got very upset at this, I stomped out of the room and made a great deal of noise going up the stairs and Da said Ah now and the next time we were down the shops Mam let me pick out the fish and she said Now pet wouldn't you be a great fishmonger altogether.

I used to say I wanted children when I grow up, I would say that when I was having tea parties with my teddies Button and Mr. Bear who is the one with the smart corduroy jumper I got at the croquet, I would pour them some tea and I would say When I grow up I'll have one hundred babies all in a big house, I was very keen on it, and then one day Mam went into hospital and came back with one and she said to me and Diarmuid This is your new brother Cathal and she put him into my arms and right then and there he soiled his nappy and that was when I began to think that having a hundred babies wasn't such a good idea after all.

But I'm very good at my subjects, maths I like well enough and sport I don't mind either, I'm very good at the skipping, but my best I'd say is spelling. Once the nuns all had us line up against the walls of the class and they went around and gave us each a word and if we misspelt it we'd have to sit down and wasn't I the next to last one standing, and the only girl to beat me was Margaret Quinn who lives in Henrietta Street the poshest street in Dublin, so really that doesn't count. And as a prize the nuns gave me a green leather daybook with gold all on the edges of the pages, a very attractive article, and I showed it to my teddies Button and Mr. Bear and they approved. I went to tell my parents the news, my uncle was in smoking with my father at the kitchen table, and I said You'll never guess what and I told them, and my father took me on his knee and said Now pet that's grand and my uncle asked what was the word I got wrong and I told him it was "column" and he said Ah now you'll excuse me for saying so but that's a damn difficult one, not sure if I could've spelt it at your age if you put it to me directly, and when Mam came in the room she said What's this I hear about Roisín being a great one for the spelling, and after tea she fixed me a drinking chocolate which normally she wouldn't do on account of she says it makes me excitable, and I nearly spilt it on my green leather daybook but I didn't.

We play games in the park, me and Diarmuid, Phoenix Park or St. Anne's Park either, we skip stones and climb in the trees and count magpies One for sorrow, Two for joy. And we say rhymes too, "Sing a Song of Sixpence" and "Monday's Child." And I say I am Monday's child, fair of face, and he says You are not you are Wednesday's child, full of woe, and I call him a bald-faced liar and I throw a rock at him.

In the summer we go over to Cork where my father's from, to Bandon and Drimoleague and Innishannon and all those places, and Diarmuid is always hogging the seat in the back of the car until by the time we've reached Cork City the two of us have nearly killed each other and the baby's crying and Mam says Holy mother of divine Jesus Liam why did we ever have children at all. And in Cork what we do is go about to different houses visiting aunts and uncles and cousins and cousins of cousins. Mam and Da have adult conversations over tea while me and Diarmuid and the cousins our age get turfed out to play rounders, or if it's raining we lay on the floor by the peat fire and have a game of cards, snap, or beggar-my-neighbor or 45, and Diarmuid always asks Why can't we play 110 and I say very matter-of-fact Because gambling's a mortal sin. And the aunts and uncles and cousins and cousins of cousins are always taking us aside and saying Now here you are love and don't tell your mother and father I gave you this and stuffing five or ten pound notes into our hands, and they say Now don't spend it all on sweets but we do, or else we leave them in our pockets and Mam finds them when she's doing the washing and she says Now who in blazes gave you that and she uses it to buy us winter coats or sensible shoes and makes us write thank-you letters in fancy joined-up writing besides.

And when we're in Cork Da is always at me for the Irish, he was raised with it after all, he'll ask me to make him a *cupan tae gan siúcra*, a cup of tea without sugar, or he'll give me some money and say Go down to the shops and buy some *prátaí agus ispíní*, potatoes and sausages, and I'll stick my tongue out at him but I'll fetch them all the same and when I come back he'll pat me on the head and say *Maith thú, maith thú*. And I always cry when it's our last day in Cork, I say Can't we stay one more night and Da picks me up and says No my love we can't, and I cry and I cry, I don't even fight with Diarmuid in the car I'm so sad, I miss the peat fires and the cows with the long eyelashes and the nights at the town disco, girls on one side, boys on the other, and the barman selling minerals and packets of crisps, and five and ten pound notes crinkling in my pocket, and I think I could be a farmer there, I could buy a farm in the country with a big house and an Aga with a laundry Sheila over it, and Mam and Da and my teddies could live there and Cathal and Diarmuid too if they were very good, and on weekends I would go into town and be a fishmonger, and I would not have a hundred babies but instead maybe a hundred sheep, and also many cows.

GLYN MAXWELL

Emily Dickinson Lesson

Heath   Samira

Lula   Ollie

Barry   Caroline

Kevin   Iona

moi

Why can't you all sit in the same damn places every week?

"*I* can't *all* do anything," Lula points out like some stroppy punk Alice.

Okay let's not use cards, let's use dice. Write down the numbers 1 to 6. Five of the faces are people in this room, you can include me if you want to, also yourself. And the 6 is God. You include Him whatever. What? Yes. Or Her. Or Them. Or It. Look the sixth face is something beyond these walls, you name it yourself. Fate, time, the stars, the weather.

So let's go round the room. Say 1 is me, 2 is Kevin, 3 is Barry, 4 is Lula, 5 is Heath, 6 is whatever God is to You, okay?

That's my version, do your own.

Now write another 1 to 6.

1 is *Love For*. 2 is *Hatred Of*. 3 is *Pity For*. 4 is *Envy Of*. 5 is *Fear Of*. 6 is *Hots For*. Are you getting the picture?

As these dice are enough for the game, these four walls and floor and ceiling are enough for the world. This is all there is. The black-dots-on-white die: people. White-dots-on-black die: emotion.

Samira raises her hand and asks: "Are these going to be poems, professor?"

Of course. They're going to be four-line poems, rhymed ABAB.

(A communal groan)

"Nursery rhymes," Heath says.

Yeah for nursery slopes (I say because he's getting on my nerves)

Samira puts her hand up again: "It's hard enough having to falsify an emotion about someone you don't want to write about, but—formal constraints as well?"

You're right. Let's make it harder. Mention only what's in this room.

Consternation: "Nothing's in the room!"

Nine chairs, table, kettle, mugs, fridge, clock, windows, pen and paper, and the race-memory of a Twix wrapper. Oh, and not forgetting that Nothing's in the room.

I weather the groans like a port in a storm. You can't teach the poet I'm teaching.

EXACTLY ONE HUNDRED YEARS BEFORE I LIVED, a woman in a small Massachusetts town came across an article in *The Atlantic Monthly* and realized that it was, in theory, addressed to her.

It was asking her for poems.

> *Letter to a Young Contributor.*
> *My dear young gentleman or young lady,—for many are the Cecil Dreemes of literature who superscribe their offered manuscripts with very masculine names in very feminine handwriting,—it seems wrong not to meet your accumulated and urgent epistles with one comprehensive reply, thus condensing many private letters into a printed one. And so large a proportion of*

"Atlantic" readers either might, would, could, or should be "Atlantic" contributors also...

At considerable length, a literary critic named Thomas Wentworth Higginson sought to explain to all the aspiring writers out there—you, me, and so forth—what kind of poetry might make it into the pages of *The Atlantic Monthly*. He urged the young hopefuls to "charge your style with life" and weeks later there came in the mail, from that same woman in Massachusetts, four odd little poems and a note: "Mr Higginson, are you too deeply occupied to say if my Verse is alive?"

YOU CAN'T TEACH EMILY DICKINSON, YOU CAN'T write like her either. You no more have to write in her stanzas than you have to write limericks or clerihews. But you do have to absorb that she wrote about *everything she could think of*—herself, others, life, death, God, Time, being here, being gone—in little quatrains shaped like hymns, rhymed or half-rhymed, mostly four beats then three beats, four, three, stanza-break, and she barely left her bedroom.

She finished her chores, had lunch, went upstairs, and sat down at a desk about the size of a tea-tray. She had two windows overlooking the one town she lived in. That was pretty much it, give or take a term in South Hadley and a short trip to Philly. Her only niece, Mattie, had a childhood memory of entering that room with her. Aunt Emily closed the door behind them, mimed the act of locking it, and said: "Mattie, here's freedom."

What you should be asking yourself is this: what is there so mighty and demanding in *you*—by which I also mean *me*—that calls for such a vast plenitude of forms? Are you more complex, do you see from wider angles, have you solved her questions?

What you owe to such a poet is a true pause for thought.

Face the wonder of her narrow choice before you run bewildered from it. For it's narrow like a ray of the sun.

And when you've finished running, from rhyme, from form, from repetition, from silence or stillness or the abstract nouns that some vague sense of the Modern has told you you can't use any more—as if your use of concrete nouns is the last word in exactitude—when you've finished running from all that and are panting with your freedom, or sweating from the demands of your so complicated life-scape, at least sit down at your own tea-tray and try writing *the present second*—

> I heard a Fly buzz—when I died—
> The Stillness in the Room
> Was like the Stillness in the Air—
> Between the Heaves of Storm—
>
> The Eyes around—had wrung them dry—
> And Breaths were gathering firm
> For that last Onset—when the King
> Be witnessed—in the Room—
>
> I willed my Keepsakes—Signed away
> What portion of me be
> Assignable—and then it was
> There interposed a Fly—
>
> With Blue—uncertain stumbling Buzz—
> Between the light—and me—
> And then the Windows failed—and then
> I could not see to see—

Yes we can note the glories—do it—her infinite narrow way of *I* along which all things travel—evoking the Wonderchild *to whom it occurs to write* "when I died"—the vast O in *Onset* as the mouth's one option when the last breaths are gathering— the words that forlornly spread themselves, entreating the moment to slow: *Keepsakes, Assignable, interposed*—the use of *Be* in "King/Be witnessed," which falls outside of mortal Time— try "Was" or "Is" to see what I mean—those last brave shots at aural unendingness: *Fly, Buzz, me, failed*—and, above all, the profound humility of the dashes—removing from the poet the grand assuming cloak of power to begin or end *anything*—stick a full-stop at the end and you've shot the thing like the Fly who killed Cock-Robin.

So much for the glories. Higginson, shaken, wrote her back with guarded encouragement but found it hard to see "what place ought to be assigned in literature to what is so remarkable, yet so elusive of criticism." He couldn't make her out at all. Eventually he had to go to Amherst to look her in the eye, for she wouldn't travel. At the door she gave him two lilies and said: These are my introduction. *Forgive me if I am frightened; I never see strangers, and hardly know what I say.*

He knew he was in the presence of the unique. Later he would say he'd never met "with any one who drained my nerve power so much. Without touching her, she drew from me. I am glad not to live near her."

And yet to Mattie, the niece, "Aunt Emily stood for *indulgence*."

Despite Higginson's interest she had virtually nothing published. That which was was altered for the worse to match conventions of the day. Bullet-hole full-stops. You can still find those versions, it's like trooping to the churchyard to stand by her grave, as I did with my Amherst students in the small hours on her birthday. But read her as she meant you to and she's standing right beside you.

She left her bedroom for good in 1886. Her sister Lavinia found eighteen hundred little poems locked away in a chest.

LET'S LOCK *YOU* IN A ROOM WITH your freedom.

Like in all my games and exercises, cards or dice stand in for fate and circumstance, and you play the role of Human Item Stuck on a Shred of Time.

So go on, shake. Shake.

Kevin: Hatred of Caroline.	("Oh—")
Barry: Envy of Glyn.	("How now, brown cow?")
Lula: Pity for Samira.	("Really?")
Heath: Love for Caroline.	("Oh jesus...")
Samira: Hots for Lula.	("Mm-*hm*. I see.")
Ollie: Fear of God.	("Woo, terrified!")
Caroline: Hatred of Lula.	("Oh no must I?")
Iona: Pity for Ollie.	(starts writing)

Is everybody happy? You bet your life you are. Express that one emotion using the form I gave you and the things inside the room. Amaze yourself. Bother me. Leave them in my box in Kerri's office. I won't share them with anyone, this is you against a dice-throw. In all my exercises the benefit is half in your resentment and three-quarters in your effort, it doesn't matter how I think you did. If you do it you win, if you don't the— Windows—fail—

And with that I'm off to the station.

IT'S AT THE SOUTH END OF THE village. I've always assumed I came by railway because I was walking north from it when I began here. It's a very small station, an old green stone building by the line. There's no name on the name-sign, just room for it. There are benches on some paving-stones and that'll do for a platform. There's a path on the rails to the other side, then a wild-flower meadow sloping away and some little patterned cows far off against the autumn mist. Sunlight never came today, the lightest clouds are low and dull in the sky to my right. I can just make out the lakeshore in the distance. To the left the ground rises into wooded hills, and I see a tunnel entrance over yonder in the distance, blue on the grey hillside. I sigh and then in silence a tiny train appears.

> I like to see it lap the Miles—
> And lick the Valleys up—
> And stop to feed itself at Tanks—
> And then—prodigious step
>
> Around a Pile of Mountains—
> And supercilious peer
> In Shanties—by the sides of Roads—
> And then a Quarry pare
>
> To fit its sides
> And crawl between
> Complaining all the while
> In horrid—hooting stanza—
> Then chase itself down Hill—
>
> And neigh like Boanerges—
> Then—prompter than a Star
> Stop—docile and omnipotent
> At its own stable door—

I await a small frail lady in white as the train slows down and grinds and stops. Then when no one descends at all, why would they—*one* does, slender and straight, from the very last carriage in a dark blue shawl and with her hair tied up. Once on the platform, some forty yards along, she goes on looking at the train, and then watches it pull away and leave her all alone. She seems so intent on doing this I stop walking, and we wait until the train has quite curved out of sight behind me, as if we can't begin until we've ceased to dwell on how we came. I resume walking toward her, and am suddenly proud to be dead, or in a coma, or in a dream, and must resist saying so, must resist saying so,

Miss Dickinson it's a dream to make your acquaintance!

She is pointing at her little feet: "I resolved to be sensible, so I wore thick shoes," and I burst out like an idiot *I* lived five years in Amherst! I lived on Dana Street! I taught in Johnson Chapel!

She raises her eyes from her shoes, not quite so far as to catch my eye, and says: "Old Time wags on pretty much as usual at Amherst."

The pleasantries I spout next I'm embarrassed to relate even here, but I manage to remember to take her little round suitcase, and enquire about her journey.

"The folk looked very funny. Dim and faded, like folks passed away."

Weird that.

We're walking along the lane, myself and Emily Dickinson, who focuses mainly on her walking feet in their sensible shoes, with occasional glances up ahead.

"The world's full of people traveling everywhere."

Tell me about it!

"Until it occurs to you that you'll send an errand, then by hook or crook you can't find any traveler to carry the package."

Totally. I mean I know.

"It's a very selfish age, that's all I can say about it."

There's a spark in her voice that suggests she might be kidding, and I steal a glance at her but don't receive one back.

You're staying at the Saddlers Inn, Miss Dickinson. They do a good eggs florentine I mean they do eventually.

While I resolve to jump in the lake later, she sighs: "I could keep house very comfortably if I knew how to cook!"

I know. Me too. Totally. You can see the inn in the distance there…

We reach the Cross and she stops, turns and looks all four ways like I would.

"October's a mighty month," she says. Then she asks where there's a library.

(I don't know where there's a library.) Let's get you checked in, yes, then I'll see if the library's open. The reading's at eight, in the village hall. There's some other stuff going on tonight, usual things on a Thursday, but my poetry group will be there, heigh-ho, so a small keen high-class crowd!

WE JINGLE THROUGH THE DOOR OF THE Saddlers Inn, whereupon Kerri stands up smartly from a table to escort our Guest to Reception. I get to sit down for a second, stare clean out of my mind through the windows and find life's splendors too bright to bear. I actually do this in Angel too, and the Garden City and New York City, not just in dreams and comas.

My vacant stare can't help but fill up with strangers, and a group of several walk by the Inn, interesting faces, various ages, a rag-tag bunch, and one who stops, frowns, peels off from the gang and here she comes, Mimi, in her black suede jacket with tassels, a death-stare to the closing door for jingling in her wake.

"Why aren't you teaching, Max, Orlando's at your class."

Collected our visitor, look.

Mimi sits down opposite and glances over at the small woman stooping to sign the register: "Woo. Legend."

You remember her?

"You taught me, didn't you. *Zero at the bone*. When's her reading."

Eight. Can I ask you something? Why don't people drink in here? It's nice and peaceful.

"Answer supplied with question," she goes.

Cross Keys is a bit grim.

"We like upsetting Norman. He hates students and he hates drinking so we pile in and order cocktails on account."

Fair enough. Who were all them?

"'Who were all them?' Glad I took a course with *you* Max. They're the actors from my course. I don't mean actors, they're just freaks doing what I do."

Why don't you take *my* course again? Killer reading series, look.

"Nah I want to try acting. Anyway I can always come to your stuff, it's not like it's official, we don't get credits."

You *can come, are you going to*?

"To her? Hell yes. Moneypenny wants you."

Over at Reception, Kerri's quietly beckoning. The boy at the bar is querying something, while Emily has drifted off to peer at the cheap prints on the walls.

She's signed herself in *Mrs Adam, Amherst*, which got the desk-boy confused.

It's fine, I say, she can say she's who she likes. Right, Miss Dickinson?

We wrongly assumed she'd heard none of this, instead of all, and she turns again with that downward smile not quite meeting our eyes: "I've lately come to the conclusion that I'm Eve, alias Mrs Adam."

Neither Kerri nor the boy understand why she'd say that, but Mimi snorts with appreciation from across the room, so Emily waves this cheerfully her way: "You know there's no account of her death in the Bible. Why am I not Eve?"

Mimi grins in support, while Kerri offers to show our Guest upstairs to the Bluebell Room. As they're ascending out of earshot I slide in opposite my former student rolling her roll-up.

Not going to smoke that in here, are you?

"Not going to say that in here, are you, so look I have this problem," and she takes out a piece of pale blue paper, flattens it face up. "Been sent this valentine that's just a fail in three ways. First I don't do valentines, second it's October, three it blows."

(I read it and well yes) Why do you think it's a valentine, it doesn't say it is.

"Alright it's just a poem, but still Max, come on, it's got *love* in it look."

Is it from Orlando?

"Yeah alright four ways."

Why don't you ask him to stop?

She licks along her liquorice rizla, "I want him to know he ought to."

How will he if you don't tell him?

"If I tell him it's too late."

Like you say, you have a problem. What can I do?

"Not your circus, not your monkeys. Can I smoke this out in the world?"

Yes Mimi, sure. You smoke it out in the world.

I FORGOT TO ASK HER WHERE THE library was, but it didn't matter for when Kerri brought our guest—now all in white and looking much more like herself—treading down from upstairs, round about the tables and out through the jingling door, the Library's where we were heading.

Kerri asked polite questions on the way:

"How long have you been away from home, Miss Dickinson?"

"Been nearly six weeks," she said briskly, then I felt her voice begin to clot with sorrow, "a longer time than I was ever away. Kind of *gone-to-Kansas* feeling."

Not over the rainbow then (say I), we're walking east we three, over the Cross, leaving the pub behind on the left, and then upward on a slight gradient, curving into trees. It's getting quite gloomy by now, more blue than grey, and I'm pretending I know there'll come a library soon—but everything else is real, and the small voice I hear is even running with my thoughts.

"I was very homesick for a few days, but I'm now quite happy. If I can be happy when absent from my... I have a very dear home. Love for them sets the blister in my throat."

That'll do it for sure.

We seem to have passed the outskirts of the village now, the last houses, a barn or two, and I'm wondering where this library is, where the signs are, what the time is, when we reach a little collection of stalls set back in a leafy space all carpeted with colored mats. There are old books on every stall, twelve stalls, volumes and volumes, and great swathes of canvas thrown back behind the hardwood frames as if to protect them when needed. They'll be needed soon, the day is ending and there's dampness in the air.

This is all the library is.

I mean to say that aloud but don't know if it's a question, or a horrified question, or a sad statement, or a sigh of the times. The reaction of our visitor sends all those four packing, for she just stares, palms raised, in on a miracle, quoting in delight: *"And I saw the Heavens opened..."*

She advances on the first stall and starts to trace her finger along the spines, as Kerri murmurs to me discreetly "Keep an eye on the clock..."

We've got a good hour, I say cheerily, we've got a *wondrous* hour.

"Wondrous forty minutes," goes Kerri, doing up her coat.

"An hour for books," says Emily, absorbed.

She starts finding things of interest: eight big black volumes of Shakespeare—"why clasp any hand but this?"—a battered blue book she takes and weighs in her palm—"of Poe I know too little to think"—a tattered Byron with the spine gone—"I've heard it argued that the poet's genius lay in his foot, as the bee's prong and his song...are you stronger than these?"—right at me, making me stronger from foot to forehead—then a dozen hefty red titles—"Father gave me quite a trimming about Charles Dickens and these modern literati"—which of course we all three smile at for different reasons, especially when she wags her finger and sounds an old soul's Yankee voice: "nothing compared to past generations that flourished when *I* was a boy!"

She reads for a while and I try not to stare at her reading. Kerri stamps her feet a bit to show it's cold and time's troops are marching by. I ask Emily if her parents encouraged her to read, and she closes the book she was reading. "My mother doesn't care for thought, and father…" She sets the book back neatly where it was. "Too busy with his briefs to notice what we do. He buys me many books but begs me not to read them, he fears they joggle the mind."

The wind gets up and dark leaves blow about her ankles. She watches till they settle.

"No one taught me," she says.

I feel a drop of rain. It's too dark to read a thing now.

She asks how one may borrow from this library and we both simply spread our hands to say *do what on earth you please*, so she chooses a dense little brown volume from the shelf, comes over and drops it straight into Kerri's coat pocket. I could see the name on the spine in golden, GEORGE ELIOT, but not which one it was, and I'd forget to ever ask. But "a little granite book to lean on," was what she said to Kerri. Then she insisted on joining in with us pulling the covers over the stalls, and tying them in place with all these frayed black ropes.

> "My life closed twice before its close—
> It yet remains to see
> If Immortality unveil
> A third event to me.
>
> So huge, so hopeless to conceive
> As these that twice befell.

>Parting is all we know of heaven,
>And all we need of hell."

Her voice doesn't so much cease as disappear and she sits down between the tall lit candles in the chilly hall. We burst into acclaim, I start musing on whether it's possible to rig up applause on a loop, which I could maybe control from a switch at my seat. For this will never bloody suffice. I make do with clapping like a loon, nobly supported by my tiny class (or most of them, Barry's not turned up again, nor has Samira, nor Ollie) along with two or three *Academy* girls at the front including long fair Isabella my one-time student. The desk-boy from the Inn came, bless him, but I see him creeping out now the reading's over. Mimi slid in at the back about halfway through, the worse for wear I thought, and loudly requested "that one with the fly" to which request the poet politely acceded.

I'm afraid the applause will stop if I stop, so I twine my arm through a chair-back to carry it to the stage and keep clumsily clapping away. When I lower the chair down nearby the poet I'm still at it, last man standing, then I sit.

A quite incredible reading, Miss Dickinson! I'm sure you all have questions before we adjourn to the Saddlers Inn? So, any questions...

This, as in all poetry readings, silences Creation.

How about I start us off... Um, Miss Dickinson, this maybe sounds silly, well it does now—ha!—but what do you like to have *around* you when you write?

"For companions?"

I nod and she smiles downward as if she'll say nothing... Then:

"Hills, and the sundown, and a dog as large as myself, that my father bought me."

The audience love this, and she looks right at them. "They're better than beings, because they know but don't tell."

A dog person not a cat person then (I play safe to the pet lobby) and Emily shudders to confirm the impression: "My ideal cat has a huge rat in its mouth, just going out of sight."

Some dog-lovers sway with vindication as she adds: "though going out of sight in itself has a peculiar charm," which leaves everyone blankly smiling. "Carl would please you," she tells the front row about her dog, "he's dumb, and brave."

One of the Academy girls asks with biro poised: "Miss Dickinson whom would you regard as your main influences."

She smiles: "For poets I have Keats, and Mr. and Mrs. Browning" (and Lula happily hisses *"Keats!"* along the chairs to show them she remembers life a week ago), "for prose, Mr. Ruskin, Sir Thomas Browne, and the *Revelations*."

"What about Whitman?" Heath asks flatly, as if she had it coming.

She puts her hands together in her lap. "Mr. Whitman, Mr. Whitman..." she ponders, only to reveal with quite a fierce little smile to no one, "I never read his book but was told it was *disgraceful!*"

Her new devotees laugh who've not read him either, but Heath has, and sits there. She seems to notice his stillness:

"Perhaps you smile at me. I had no monarch in my life, and can't rule myself."

Heath looks uncomfortable and nods by way of support.

"Could you tell me how to grow?" she asks him, innocent of mischief.

Blindsided, he looks grave, stares away, quits the field.

"Or is it unconveyed," she says, looking up at the rafters, "like melody or witchcraft... I've no tribunal."

All smile amiably as she passeth understanding.

Breezily I ask if she follows world affairs, and she makes that clear as day: "Won't you please tell me who the candidate for President is?"

We all mention names you know and the candles cringe with shame.

"I don't know anything more about the affairs in the world than if I were in a trance. Do you know of any nation about to besiege South Hadley? If so, do inform me—I'd be glad of a chance to escape, if we're to be stormed."

Out of the laughter Caroline ventures: "Emily, if I may, when you say your soul selects its own society, do you mean you rather prefer your own company to, well, to company? Do you think you have a tendency to avoid people?"

I don't expect her to agree quite but what do I know? "They talk of hallowed things, aloud, and embarrass my dog. He and I don't object to them, if they'll exist their side."

Lula likes it and ventures "How d'you like *know* good poetry when you see it?"

Emily shakes her head slowly, then breathes in sharply—"If I—read a book and it makes my whole body so cold no fire can ever warm me, I know that's poetry. If I feel physically as if—the top of my head were taken off! I know that's poetry. These are the only ways I know it. Is there any other way?"

The consensus murmurs there is not, and then she closes her eyes and sighs from memory: "Though earth and man were gone, and suns and universes ceased to be, and Thou wert left alone, every existence would exist in Thee."

(There's a space for mooing in awe which is duly filled, while I find some recklessness to hand) Is that a new poem, Miss Dickinson?

She smiles sadly, and it hits me too late, not hers at all—

"Gigantic Emily Brontë…" (We all nod, we knew that) "Of whom Charlotte said: 'Full of ruth for others, on herself she had no mercy.'"

Caroline is nodding wisely, and Lula pipes up: "Bit random but: when you say about hearing a fly when you died right?

which is *mentally* good, and about life closing twice and that? like, what is it you *mean* if that's not moronic."

Emily frowned, then thought, then said she'd tell a little story, of a woman who came to her door in Amherst one morning, "an Indian woman with gay baskets and a—dazzling baby, at the kitchen door. Her little boy 'once died' she said, death to her—*dispelling* him. I asked her what the baby liked, and she said—'to step.'"

Lula devilishly shivers, when a husky voice from the back inquires: "You ever send a valentine?"

The audience frowns and giggles and turns, enjoying that question, and I notice both Caroline and Heath staring back curiously at unbothered Mimi for longer than they need to. I assumed everyone knew everyone, as we do when we know no one.

Sure she sent a valentine:

"Put down the apple, Adam, and come away with me; so shalt thou have a pippin from off my father's tree..."

She may not have meant to but she says this straight at Kevin, who visibly freezes in the beam. His eyes are wider than I've seen them. His shy paralysis seems to slow the atmosphere, and though she's no longer looking at him, the expression on his face is *you and me in the dark together*—out of which she lifts a gem for him and him only: "I work to drive the awe away. Yet—awe—impels the work."

ON THE SHORT WALK TO THE SADDLERS from the village hall—Emily suggested we prolong it by walking the long way clockwise round the lamp-lit oval green—several of her listeners made their private move toward her side, but I noticed that the one she sought out and found was Heath. By the time I reached them, rather fearing he might be indelicate or rude in some way, they were parting most politely: "I've read nothing of

Turgenev's," I heard her say, "but thank you for telling me—I will seek him immediately."

She then walked some slow yards with Iona McNair, who said she liked that bracelet very much, and the poet, having touched Iona's white scarf and wondered at the material, said gaily: "Santa Claus was *very* polite to me last Christmas. I hung up my stocking on the bedpost as usual—I had a perfume bag, a bottle of otto-of-rose to go with it, a sheet of music, a china mug with Forget me not upon it, a watch case..." she couldn't remember for a moment and now everyone was listening... "Abundance of candy! Also two hearts at the bottom of it all, which I thought looked rather ominous."

Lula came up explaining why last Christmas in Camden Town was a *total mare*, then asked her, before I could do anything, how she went about being published, to which Emily cheerfully pronounced: "Two editors of journals came to my father's house and asked me for my mind, and when I asked them *why*—they said they'd use it for the world."

She chuckled at this sufficing answer, so Lula did, actually I did, then one of the Academy girls quickened her pace and asked if Emily enjoyed a bit of—we couldn't catch what—to which she said: "To live is so startling, it leaves little room for other occupations!" and all wondered and jested as to what had been asked, jingling and jangling into the inn so pleased they'd chosen to attend.

WE'D LOST A FEW BY NOW. KEVIN, who had shied away—*shying* was Kevin's active verb—Heath, who parted from the poet with a stiff male bow from some bygone century in his mind, the Academy girls who'd got all their answers, and Mimi, who'd had her fun. Lula, Bella, Iona, and Caroline sat down around a table set for tomorrow's breakfast. The desk-boy listened from Reception as he doodled in a ledger. Our company was briefly augmented by Barry Wilby, who dropped by to make his apologies—"duties, Teacherman, beaucoup de duties"—and wanted to ask "Mrs. Dixon where she gets her ideas"—but at that point I called a halt, for the lady looked fatigued and on our time not hers.

All four women rose to escort her upstairs, and Barry cried "Another day!" and though I summoned up the speech to tell her how I felt, by the time those words came in their nervous Sunday best I stood alone, in the cold on the lamp-lit Village Green, watching her one amber square of light go on in the wooden roof of the inn. I'd done all I could do with a smile. I didn't expect to be here in the morning. I waited till her room went dark.

ON THE WAY BACK I SWING BY Student Services—Kerri's given me a key now and I can pick up what's there. These are.

> *Samira Sharma: "I Have the 'Hots' for Lula"**
>
> *If we all spent a night in here*
> *I would stay awake until you sleep*
> *and then I would overcome my fear*
> *and cut a red hair for me to keep.*
> *(*I do not have the hots for Lula.)*
>
> *Pity for Orlando (Iona McNair, Poetry/Maxwell)*
>
> *I don't think—I can risk it—*
> *It is not—my Place to say—*
> *But I want to give that boy—this Biscuit—*
> *And tell him—Things will be okay—*

I collect them, as if I'll need them, if I'm dead I may well need them, and I lock the office behind me.

AT THE END OF HIS *Letter to A Young Contributor* Thomas Higginson wrote the following, and I thought I'd tape it to my bedroom wall before turning in for the night. He couldn't figure out anything either—and with his one great Young Contributor he both grasped and missed his chance—but he sensed there was a place where it would matter to have tried. He was a famous abolitionist.

> *War or peace, fame or forgetfulness, can bring no real injury to one who has formed the fixed purpose to live nobly day by day. I fancy that in some other realm of existence we may look back with some kind interest on this scene of our earlier life, and say to one another,—"Do you remember yonder planet, where once we went to school?"*

GEORGE KALOGERIS

Antigone

A handbook for the soul no one can read.
A vale that's watered by tears. A private school
For deaf-blind children, in Brookline, where I worked,

Part-time, with a stubborn little girl in constant agony,
Profoundly autistic, the one we called *Antigone*.
She always wore a helmet, even while sleeping,

Because, as an infant, she'd blinded herself with her fists.
An orange, perforated, styrofoam helmet
To ward off the sleepless demons inside her head.

(It's one thing to sing the form the frightened hare
Once left in the melting snow, another to wince
At a hare-lip whose trembling cleft will never depart.)

If she wasn't held, or strapped to a chair with restraints,
She'd batter her eyes and ears, her nose and mouth,
As if she were trying to shut down all of her senses.

Little Antigone, buried alive in herself.
(O healing god of dreams, Asclepian snake,
Your cure the spell that enters through our ears:

Could you not slither through those cauliflowers?)
She signed with her hands, but only when prompted by staff.
And then always the same three frantic gesticulations

For Eat, and Drink, and More—as if anorexic
Language could only express the naked hunger
It cannot feed, as it screamed through the tongues in her hands

For Eat and Drink and More. And yet, at the sink,
With her tiny fists still clenched, she would stand calm
For a couple of hours, as the steady warm stream kept pouring

Down over her hands, until like flower buds
Her tiny fists unfurled to the faucet water.
Now the gush of it splashed against her outstretched palms—

Ecstatic stigmata—as she alternated her hands,
One over the other, as though in eloquent discourse
With the one who quenched her thirst, the Anne Sullivan

Of the shining, babbling water, the water that held her
As warm as the womb of never being born.
Her frizzy, unhelmeted hair. The faucet unfailing.

Her eyes that were never open, except at the sink.
Her pupils like grey-blue fuses of broken bulbs.
That spellbound little girl, at home in the school

For the deaf and blind, just standing there by a pair
Of gleaming knobs and the fluent, effusive water—
And looking like she'd solved the Sphinx's riddle.

MARY JO SALTER

Vierge Ouvrante

Walters Art Museum

Marvelous and a little sick
that her immaculate ivory
self is sawn into a triptych

from her uncrowned head straight down
the neck, the breastbone, and the lap
enthroning her bisected son.

Magnetic on the double-door
refrigerator of her white
body, he is miniature

but mature, an all-suffering
king already killed, reborn,
who elevates one hand in blessing

while the other must hold steady
the great globe on his knee, the whole
world that is his baby—

or will be when the world's redeemed.
But this is France, the year 1200,
and to the sculptor it has seemed

both beautiful and necessary
that the hinged, compliant Virgin
unfold the living allegory

buried in her anatomy,
as if some holy madman surgeon
scarified there, in the three

small panels, the naked guts of sin
coiled and twisting in the back
story of the coming Passion:

instead of one loved child who grows
within her, here are multiple
horror-shows, the Man of Sorrows

mocked along his bitter path,
the stations of the Cross that lead
to the death she's pregnant with.

Come the French Revolution, she
too will be a thing of scorn—
turned into a children's toy

fitted with four wheels and a cord
to pull around the Queen of Heaven.
What to do but be drawn forward

to Baltimore, where now, a vision
butterflied on her stand, she's propped
up like the one Book's one edition?

She knows the future is past mending.
Why look to her for an opening
for some other ending?

JOHN MORAN

Undeniable Sausage

Against the Surplus Value, the lavender of sunset. Inside the Surplus Value, a cold-storm wind. Everything inside Surplus Value is yellow and red: colors that stimulate primal compelling. This combination of the colors of summer and the elements of winter distorts the senses of Mary, who is already adequately distracted, adequately disoriented, adequately immobilized by a brain of commoditized plastic and the pressing power of a God everywhere invisible. In the car, Mary had put an old blouse and skirt over her bathing suit, but she is not yet dry. She is not yet like the dried fruits and nuts hanging in plastic bags clipped to red lattice by the check-out counter: the ova and sperm of blossoming trees flamboyant in the woods like floral headdresses or mating peacocks or platters of cut-up fruit: for seven cents, you too can taste a billion years' geometry.

Esther shakes her finger. "Ice." She walks past the Men's and Boy's sections of the grocery store, with the barbecue supplies, the steaks, the sausage, the whiskey wall—examining the cheap price of plastic-wrapped chicken, how it would have been cheaper to get than the damn fish they spent the day catching— to the Women's section, with the chocolate, the lemon cakes, the watermelons. The ice machine is back by the white dairy wall, a wall made one creamy milk white by endless individual gallons, like a pointillist painting, like a fascist nation, like a silkscreen printing of the future, the gift that bovines give their young diverted into equal measures, and those gallons, born as equals, into houses where they fall at different paces, in fridges made open by different smiles, half a cup into a casserole, one glass for a man to dunk his cornbread in, three cups for all the children, then all the milk left sitting in containers across the land, an inch in one gallon souring, a drop in another gallon souring, a whole gallon souring, or not a drop wasted. Then all the gallons dragged to, and buried in, the landfill of heaven, where they call out for each other, weakly, decomposing over hundreds of years, whimpering their sweet gallon song, a low mourning melody, *We were meant for the calf.*

Mary stares at the penguins printed on the ice machine, which remind her of *Mr. Popper's Penguins*. She was taken back, reading that book, by the penguins' coats. That they could be like human coats, without having to buy them. That like milk, the animal just made it. Mary had learned to say to herself, "human nature." Mom handed her a bag to carry, half her height, or at least a third. She will succeed. The bag of glaciers is too heavy for her mini-muscles. Esther takes it. Can ice think? Does it have needs? What ever made us think ice does not care? That glaciers are not social? That glaciers do not mourn when we melt them?

On a shelf by the check-in counter is a black-and-white television.

"Country's going to war again," says Ms. Linda, whom Esther and Mary know from years of buying ice and bait and white bread and preserves. "That'll be twenty cents, ma'am."

On the TV, a colored woman wails.

"What's it now," says Esther. She fishes a quarter from her pocket. There's no use carrying a purse.

"Somebody killed Martin Luther King," says Ms. Linda.

"Oh Lord," says Esther. "When?"

"Just an hour two ago. It's Vietnam come home."

When the news of the Prophet King spreads over the land, foods in the grocery store come, baby, into consciousness. The milk gallons, once a perfect wall of white, start to paint each other's bodies, gripping tubes of soulful acrylic by their handles and shuffling along the shelves, painting streaks of blue and red and yellow over their perfect porcelain bodies. Esther,

Mary, and Linda hear a chattering from the Women's section. The green beans have developed language. An eggplant finds her soul, and is now Buddhist. The fruits, vegetables, cans, bags, coming together, creating the Shelf-Space Efficiency Redistribution System: eggplants living like kings, popcorns stacked on top of each other three miles high sewing textiles for eggplants. They ignore they will be eaten. One of the pork loins goes out to the parking lot, and all the cucumbers watch it on television, "One small step for pork loins," and the cucumbers decide the store foods are magnanimous genius intelligent beautiful, it is all true, there is no truth, and the grey *National Enquirers* go to war with the silver York Peppermint Patties, and a head of lettuce bemoans Why? And someone buys her and makes her into salad, and sitting in a toilet bowl as shit, which will not regrow the Earth but instead sit making death into further death in a concrete vat, she decides she has had it with lettuce-centric ontology, and four decades later writes a post, *23 Bad Things You Didn't Know Happen to Lettuce.*

"Somebody shot the black man," says Mary, getting in the car.

"Somebody shot who?" asks Corn. He scans the horizon. "D'you see a gun?"

Esther is behind the car, throwing ice bags onto the parking lot to break them into something useful. Ice cannot think. The glaciers are as good as crushed. She puts the ice on the fish in the blood-red Coleman cooler, with the preservation and the sacred covering-up of smell.

"On the TV," says Mary.

"Where people die," says Corn.

Esther opens the front passenger door. "King is dead," she says, getting in.

Dilsey gasps. "Killed?"

"*Who* killed *who*?" asks Tammy.

"The Reverend Martin Luther King was shot, in Memphis," says Esther. "Nobody knows who."

Corn cranks the car. The energy from the shaking frame of the car rises into them through the seats that dance restrained.

"You know, that's a thing people have been saying for centuries," says Corn. "The *king* is dead. Didn't they say that when Jesus died? Had 'King' written on the cross. The King of the Jews; the King of the Coloreds; the King of the Communists." Corn thought King was an extremist, a communist outsider, who swooped in from outside and chased dramatic examples. That's how he'd always done it in Florida. Done something ridiculous, gotten himself arrested, all so he'd look a pity for the TV cameras and pinko tears'd roll down Yankee cheeks.

"Well, I am sorry, Dilsey." Esther puts her hand to her forehead. "Sorry to deliver the news and sorry it happened. I know Mr. King was an inspiration for your people."

"Yes, ma'am." Dilsey places a hand softly on the door handle. She wants to jump out and call her brother from the phone in front of Surplus Value and get a ride. But it is true, truer than true, that Panacea is not a safe place for Negroes at night. Awaframahaxee neither. Didn't Dilsey's family know that more than anybody. Didn't Esther's too. It is as if a line has been crossed—the line Jesus drew in the sand—and all bets are off. Earth is spinning different from how it's been spun. Or else it has never spun. Globe could be flat as a pancake and would you really know, really really know?

ESTHER, LISTENING TO THE CAR RADIO, AGREES with Dilsey that, "It is not safe for you to walk back to your place tonight." Esther thinks about the Negro woman who was raped, golly, it must have been a decade ago, by four white men. That girl was a student at FAMU, the black college, just like Dilsey. That the men went to jail in the late 1950s in the South was remarkable—it made national headlines. Esther is proud that the men had been convicted. Black women are women.

"My mama'll be worrying to death and beyond," says Dilsey.

"Well, we'll drop you off," says Esther. "I bet the Reverend is handling it more poorly than your mother."

"Tonight, Dilsey owes us two more hours of employment," says Corn. "We are having too many exceptions."

"Then let's fry the fish," says Esther. "If you want to go home after dinner, Corn'll drive you."

"Nobody in this house is driving anywhere tonight," says Corn. "We are heading straight home. I'm not gonna slow down. Dilsey can sleep in Tammy's room, Tammy can sleep on the sofa, I can sleep on the porch. Better yet I can sleep with the rifle. Nobody's going to school or to work or to the moon tomorrow. Dilsey, we will pay you overtime."

"I think it's best for me to sleep at my parents'," says Dilsey.

"I'm your employer," says Corn.

"I'm heading up to Rockland tomorrow," says Esther.

"There ain't no fuss ever out in Rockland," says Corn. "They got people. They don't need you so bad they can't live without you for one day."

"They do need me," says Esther.

"Are we there yet?" asks Mary. She has seen young girls say it on the television; she has read it in books. The phrase is crafted for her: it represents how she feels, it is a commodity designed for her consumption, and she loves it, and it loves her, and it fits perfect in her mouth, curling into her desperation, a candy.

They make no decision.

Esther hums a hymnal. Their station wagon is the one flash of light under the dome, piercing through the Apalachee National Forest, where pines absorb the headlights like a fun house of mirrors. They pass a sign from after the war:

FIRE:

AMERICA'S NEW ENEMY

Deer slouch in the road. Corn slows, speeds, slows, weaving through beasts. He will not honk at them, so to not disturb the forest, although the forest is always disturbed; the forest is disturbance: made by squawks and honks, by rattling and crashing, by mastication, the lick of tongues, and the thrumming of hearts, by mating and eating, and the rustling flower, by the wings alive like their car engine, by the flickers of bioluminescence like their car seeing. Their wagon is slick, a babe, with points and smooth descents like surfboards. In a few decades, in a few breaths of forest, station wagons will be all curved up, domestic, pregnant, like moms, with their back-up cameras and beeping sensors, nothing left raw, everything cooked, warmed-over. In a few breaths more, there will be no station wagons, except for metal scraps in mechanical morgues, industry ripping scraps asunder, rusted by working men's tear-sweat, which looks like powerless, limp water, but can wrap something and in a grip, corrode it, fall from the sky and return to it, fall through the finger cracks of your hand when you try to cup it, soaking in the railroad tracks where human and nonhuman labor is expropriated by the 1 percent.

Corn looks up at the moon to plan their next fishing trip. Waning gibbous. They won't be back for a while. He thinks of the two wildlife officers shot in succession by poachers in the Apalachee forest. He knew the brother of one.

Always violence in the woods. Everywhere would be woods tonight. King was an out-of-state agitator. Tallahassee has always had good race relations. There'd never been a problem. He knows firsthand from growing up in Autaguaville, up in Alabama, where things were worse. Now, Negroes deserved their rights. Hitler and Hirohito taught Corn that. The line was crossed when those little black girls died in the church bombing. But a man has got to have the freedom to choose his own associates. A man has got to have it, but it's no more. Even if a black person ain't qualified to do a job, you can't say so without fear of losing your own. The Anglo-Saxon race civilized Negroes, and now Negroes want to burn the civilization down. Rewriting history is what bothers Corn. Children these days are liable to think Anglo-Saxons and Negroes started off history holding hands, started off at the same level of development, and then there had been some terrible separation and the Negro had been deemed inferior by the terrible Anglo-Saxon. Slavery was a sin, of course it is a sin for one man to own another, but Negroes were not American before it or without it. That is a fact you cannot ignore. The American Negro is the most advanced specimen of African in all the history of the world. People will talk your head off, all afternoon, about the evil of segregation, but under segregation Negroes and whites lived closer together than they ever lived before, in all of history! Without the white man, the Negro would not read or write; the Negro would not wear clothes. Corn has spent his life surrounded by Negroes—slaughtering pigs with them, housing them, feeding them, laughing with them, drinking with them. Yes, Corn was fine to share a drink with Negroes. It made his blood boil that the TV men made it out that he hated niggers. Southerners were the only people who knew what niggers were actually like, and soon no white child would know the true history of how niggers had been civilized, because Madison Avenue was painting civilized niggers into the Garden of Eden. Used to be the separation of the races was about as obvious as oxygen. Now you got to explain and justify the very air. Liable to collapse a lung.

The kids hop up and down in the back seat laughing, because the car is an enclosure that traps their thermodynamism. Then the kids are asleep, because the car is an enclosure that traps their thermodynamism. Dilsey is calm, composed, alert. She doesn't like the Moodys. She doesn't want to be prisoner in their house just because of a human thunderstorm. They aren't good folks. They are white to the bone: using fear to get what they want. You can feel the colonizer's fear as the car plunges into the blackening air.

IN TALLY, THE LOW HONEY SUN ISN'T working too hard to bedazzle through the moss draping the trees (you could be great, sun, if only you put in a bit more effort, just a bit!). The Moodys arrive at their two-story house, which looks like it may fall in on itself, and is plastered with a large red-and-white sign that reads:

UNDENIABLE SAUSAGE:
PURVEYOR FLAVIUS CRACKER
FROM THE ROOTER TO THE TOOTER

In the yard are two campaign signs:

WALLACE FOR PRESIDENT
STAND UP FOR AMERICA

Because the house is a few generations old—Esther's family, the Crackers, came to the Panhandle during the heyday of lumber after the Civil War, then got into pigs and—because there have been several agricultural and industrial revolutions—the house appears to have been built for little people: a house with smaller frames. The tiny, thin walls chop up rooms so quaint that only the master bedroom is large enough for a double bed, and the bed fills the room. Tiny walls keep everything in its place: cooking is a small thing, and you only do it here. Loving is a quiet thing, you don't want to shake the living room. Living is a thing you do touching other people's shoulders, spread like tangled moss in a cardboard box.

They step onto the screened porch, which wraps all around the house, and walk down the hallway off the screened porch, which bisects the first floor into two separate parts: one the living area, one the store, where they purvey sausage to the fine people of Tallahassee, and have since the start of the twentieth century.

"We caught enough fish for weeks," says little Mary, as

the family opens the cooler behind the house. Dilsey walks past the fish-cleaning table into the kitchen, which is in the back of the yard. Mary stands at attention as she makes her report, as if announcing that the boats have landed at Normandy, unaware of the casualties.

"Now I don't know about for weeks," says Corn.

"Not the way you young 'uns eat," says Esther.

"At least they don't eat like boys," says Corn.

"Thank the Lord on his throne," says Esther, sick and tired of Corn's comparisons.

CORN CLEANS THE FISH AT THE TABLE out back, which is leaned-up against the house. He teaches Tammy and Mary how to clean the fish, breaking a process normally an art, like a maestro on the violin, into carefully comprehendible sequential steps, digestible like bites.

DURING THE BEST DAYS OF HER LIFE, Tammy, in her late thirties, will stand at the blood- and ice-drenched tables out back of the Awaframahaxee KOA, where she will teach her nine-year-old son Quentin and seven-year-old son Jackson to clean fish. At the drenched tables Tammy will be wistful for the mullet stains along the trunk bed of her parents' Cadillac station wagon, brimming with kids and the lace of cast nets. In these fraying neuron clusters—these antidepressant electric-blue caverns of Spanish moss—Tammy will have no symptoms of the silence of seventies-prefab suburbia ("how was your day?" "Good. I ran some errands, did some paperwork"). From her memories, Tammy will hand her son Jackson a fish eye to bounce up and down along the beach. Only stingray eyes do decent bouncing— Tammy knows this, Jackson and Quentin know she knows— so Jackson will sit on a sea wall examining the moon snail ooze around the black-pellet eye, whirling like a liquid wedding gown worn by the whites of a fried egg, like a melting member of the Klan. His brother will demand the eye. Quentin will cusp his hands around the orb of light, praying for the black nanny he never met, Dilsey's eyes looking over the big-ass speckled stockpot on the back burner, at mid-century-modern peace with the green tile counter; Dilsey's magnanimous eyes: cherry brown, cocoa brown, honey brown, nesting in the flesh of acorn shells, taking in the light.

(To survive, we have fetishized the other-eyes.)

After Quentin tosses the eye in the sea, they will run back to the tables behind the Awaframahaxee Point KOA. Tammy, like Corn before her, will teach Quentin and Jackson step two in the four-step process of whittling an animal with parents and children into the arginine and gylcine the liver needs to synthesize creatine. All Quentin will remember is that sometimes the fish tail keeps spazzing even after you cut off the head.

"SOMETIMES IT DOES THAT," CORN SAYS TO Tammy, ignoring the flapping tail of the headless fish. "Sometimes it keeps on doing it a long time. You can whack it."

"God, is this tail gonna stop?" asks Tammy.

"Don't use the Lord God's name in vain," says Corn. "If you do he will bring down wrath. Just when you think you're on top."

Corn spots a raccoon eating watermelon, between the giant pine tree and the old circus tent he'd found in the back of a Chevy truck he'd repaired and flipped. He wouldn't let the kids go down to the water because he had killed several gators, a ten-footer included, but there were more; so the tent was a godsend for the kids. Old folks had named the swamps behind the place Raccoon Lagoon, and, while it was true, Corn had taught the kids to call it Gator Lake. When they were being born they'd called it Hog Lake. During the war, Esther's father couldn't afford to keep the hogs. They released them into the woods to shoot when they could, and went out to chop down sabal palms to eat swamp cabbage. The wildness of the lagoon was a reminder to Corn that once you lose your grip on things—a wealth of hogs, a war, a nation, a sense of community peace—you never get it back. Its ghost lives under the leaves forever, and you can never eradicate or even master the wild hogs, the coons, the rebels, the perpetually dissatisfied Negro race.

"That boar coon'll kill a dog," says Corn. He throws a rock. The raccoon paces back, but once the rock is landed returns again. Corn throws a second rock. It doesn't work. Corn gets the shotgun and shoots the boar coon.

All the while, Corn is thinking about burnt fish. When its burnt, you can eat through the bones. You don't gotta waste time being delicate. The world is not fragile, not intricate. Just burn it. Disappear every trace.

Dilsey's mother, Lucilla, is setting pimento cheese sandwiches down on a foldable wood tray between the rockers in front of the bare, damp-grey fireplace. The sandwiches are next to biscuits with beautyberry jam from the yard. Beautyberry needs sugar to taste good. Sugar isn't an evil so much as a good. Lucilla does not allow her husband the Reverend to light fires because they live in Smokey Hollow, a low place where the hills trap smoke. Not that it matters keeping Smokey Hollow's air clean, since the neighborhood is being demolished by an urban renewal project, to build the towering temple of the Florida Board of Conservation, and the trailer the Reverend and Mrs. Samuel Anderson live in, owned by Corn Moody, is scheduled to be taken by eminent domain in fourteen months, for a low price. Nobody of any color is happy: neither the white folks who own the hollow, nor the black folks who live in it. She is wearing her nightgown, even though Elders Breedlove and Sapp are visiting for an emergency meeting; a protest to her husband that perhaps less visiting should be done. Although she is still scrubbed clean. Her nightgown does not excuse her son Lamarcus for grease between his thumbs. Racists always talk about the smell of niggers. You have to prove yourself with appearances. Her husband the Reverend Anderson, Pastor of Calvary, the second-largest African Methodist Episcopal Church in the city of Tallahassee, reads the King James Version of *Bad Things Happen to Adam and Eve*, thumbing his suspenders between phone calls. At the shelf, he strokes the spine of Frederick Douglass's *Bad Things Happen to Slaves*. Elder Breedlove smokes a sober cigar. The trailer is dark, in part because Corn, a negligent landlord, has not fixed the wiring to the light and ceiling fan.

"There's not a chance in the world you're going down there, young man," says Mr. Anderson to Dilsey's brother, watching his son open the door. He is worried that his son will be written up in the papers. Twelve years ago, during the bus boycotts, *The Tallahassee Mullet Wrapper* had gone after Reverend Anderson himself. Called him a communist. Took a few hours for the Reverend to find out because colored folks got a different edition of the newspaper, which, for example, lacked a business section. A year ago Reverend Anderson had been disappointed his son was not interested in Gandhi. The situation had escalated.

"Lamarcus," says Lucilla. "Please."

"You'd sit tight until Jesus returns just for the scraps on the white man's table," says Lamarcus in the doorway. Lamarcus is twenty-five and has no wife yet, which is unheard of. He is using King's death to mourn Malcolm's. He is an Afrocentrist. "It's like with Dilsey's school transfer. Here you are, in your suspenders, twirling your finger around the dial, filling out enough papers to regrow the pine forests just so your one little black daughter, who works in white people's homes anyway, can go to a white kid's school, when we got hundreds of black kids ain't never gonna have that opportunity because of your *niggardly acquiescence*."

Lamarcus shuts the door behind himself.

Lucille is upset that Lamarcus is making a show in front of their visitors, but more upset that he addresses only his father.

"I am come to send fire on the earth," says Reverend Anderson, "and what will I, if it be already kindled? But I have a baptism to be baptized with; and how am I straitened till it be accomplished! Suppose ye that I am come to give peace on earth? I tell you, Nay; but rather division: For from henceforth there shall be five in one house divided, three against two, and two against three. The father shall be divided against the son, and the son against the father; the mother against the daughter, and the daughter against the mother; the mother in law against her daughter in law, and the daughter in law against her mother in law."

"You always had a way with a line," says Lucilla, chuckling.

Reverend Anderson ignores her, continuing to pace and preach. "And he said also to the people," says Reverend Anderson, "When ye see a cloud rise out of the west, straightway ye say, There cometh a shower; and so it is. And when ye see the south wind blow, ye say, There will be heat; and it cometh to pass. Ye hypocrites, ye can discern the face of the sky and of the earth; but how is it that ye do not discern this time?"

"Hm," says Elder Breedlove.

"I never understood what He meant there," says Reverend Anderson. "Perhaps, He was saying that He himself was coming like a storm. He is a power above us, like the storm. We don't have a choice when He comes, like we don't have a choice when it rains. God is electricity. Zeus is lightning."

"Sit down," says Lucilla.

They contemplate in the dark, a thing people have done for many years, not really ever getting what's up with the universe. Reverend Anderson is thinking about Elder Breedlove. In his mind, Reverend Anderson can smell the tip of Elder Breedlove's dick. A dick he has sucked many times and would like to suck now, quick. He shudders, ashamed of his own thoughts.

A phone rings. As with a person screaming, one must answer it. The phone has been screaming the whole evening now, everyone with a question or a prayer or an idea for Reverend Anderson, magnet in the network of decency. Even white people were calling. A Unitarian Universalist minister had called. An Episcopal priest had called. The mayor had called, which was whoopty doo.

"Reverend Anderson," says Reverend Anderson.

"Hey daddy," says Dilsey.

"Why aren't you home yet?"

"I have two more hours of work, then I may stay here, unless you can pick me up."

"Maybe it's best you stay there. We sitting tight."

"How you holding up, daddy?"

"The same way I hold up on the passing of any friend, although this friend was something more. Glad we got him down to town during the meetings. But I don't know what we are gonna do. The country has storms building out over the water."

"It's not gonna get any better with you saying that."

Reverend Anderson stares up at the dead light. Corn Moody, his own landlord, and a decent man, too, used to be on the Citizens Council, which was basically the Klan but with their shoes shined. Reverend Anderson had wanted to move for a long time, but it would have cost them in quality of life. They couldn't get a place like this for the price they had, and Mr. Moody didn't raise their price. He might be the most principled man in town, truth be told. But the Reverend had made a deal with the devil for the roof over their head. He did it for Lucilla, who did it for the children. The world's problems grow because children brew loyalty, jealousy, fierce guardianship.

"You're right. Darling, could you please tell Mr. Moody that when he gets a chance, not on this dark night, but perhaps on some near dawn, it would be *most appreciated* if he could change our ceiling fixture? We may be in the darkness of injustice, but we would like to read the newspaper with something brighter than a flicker of hope."

Once upon a time he would've been worried about Dilsey offending Corn and jeopardizing her job. Now he wanted her gone from that job anyway. She wasn't going to be a science teacher if she spent her working hours doing women's work.

"Y'all need to march to FAMU right now and end this mess," says Lucilla. "All three of you."

"Our time is passed," says Reverend Anderson. You work for progress your whole youth, you are always on the frontline, and no matter how far you tread, by the end of it all, you will be a dusty irrelevant relic, watching society do what you didn't want it to do. Ain't it arrogant to think you can control history? The flow of time? Those waters of the Lord that restore us all—you think you can build a little dam across them, redirect them to a little pond for yourself where you can have a stock of catfish? Reverend Anderson is trying to control the energy inside himself, much less history. He feels a wave inside. He is hopping on his legs like a guy drinks a whole pot of coffee. "You okay?" He barely hears Lucilla ask. His limbs loosen from his control, free like marine creatures. He's melting into air and feels an energy inside him cascading feverishly from his forehead to the wet insides of his elbows, where he lays a tender finger to make sure he still exists. There's a tightening in his thighs, they're heavy now, they're centering energy on his dick like he is about to be stimulated. His thighs try to hold up the collapsing colossus of his lightened, angelic breast. The last thing he feels before slipping into his dreams is the tight embrace of Elder Breedlove. The Elder is behind him, the Elder's hot breath in his hair, the Elder's magnificent arms tight around his chest, pulling him gently to the ground. The Reverend has never felt so warm. His whole body would erupt out of its skin in orgasm if it could, shedding his life—his race, his name, his wife—like a snake.

Down there, in the swamps where visions ferment, swirling across the watery film, flows tugged by cosmic gravity, Reverend Anderson sees one of the Easter Island statues—except it is head of the Reverend Dr. Martin Luther King Jr. Brown instead of stone. Just as wise. He turns 'round. The statue seems to be in the jungle—the ground is moist soil, the plants are excessive, with giant leaves and fragrance—but there is the White House. The actual White House. The statue of Reverend King is there in DC, towering over the Mall, surrounded by Lincoln, Jefferson, Washington, but overgrown. Reverend Anderson kneels, prostrate before King, like a Roman Catholic or a Moslem. *He was sent by God*, Reverend Anderson hears himself say. *He is the son of God returned. He came to lead his people. He is the most high King. Found a Church. The Church of the King. Do you feel the King? I feel him. Do you feel the King? Let Earth rejoice! He shall return!*

The Reverend Anderson comes back. He is still in Elder Breedlove's arms. He shouts with joy and claps his hands. Elder Breedlove helps him up. Reverend Anderson realizes his dick his hard, like he has just woke. He moves right to his chair, crossing his legs to hide it.

"The fire has rained down on this house tonight," he says. "I know what to do. I know what to do. We have been called by the Lord. We've been called. Brothers and sisters, there is a fire that was shielded from today's storm, and we will keep the flame."

His wife, Lucilla, looks from her husband's crotch to Elder Breedlove's shoulders, and back again.

DILSEY'S BROTHER, LAMARCUS, GOT A FRO, SWEAT in his fro, he's in a crowd, under the oaks of Florida Agricultural and Mechanical University, the Negro school, 'cause Negroes have a seat at the table beyond picking weeds and fixing cars and wiping white ladies' kitchens and white babies' asses, do they now? You think they was gonna name it Florida Doctoring and Lawyering School for Whip-Smart Coloreds? Lamarcus's bent over the trunk of a red Pontiac unloading crates of empty coke bottles, dusty temples of dusky syrup, clinking odes to sweet nickels down throats and machines, and rags: stolen from somebody and everybody's mother, drenched in oil and butter and egg and the sea, rags done their duty on Thanksgiving, wiped things you don't care to know about. His fraternity brother, James, takes bottles out of the crate, pouring gas from the red can he filled at Amoco. He douses the rags in alcohol and stuffs them in the necks of the coke bottles. Fuck these racist mothafuckas.

Lamarcus and James join the crowd marching down Gaines Street. The march reminds Lamarcus of when he had participated at a sit-in at the Woolworth's lunch counter when he was a high schooler. He had been arrested and walked to the police station like a parade. Whites had booed and jeered from their shops. They did not boo and jeer tonight. The city was locked down. Gas stations and liquor stores were closed. The president of FAMU had, just two hours before, ordered the university closed, for a week, so that tensions might cool. They were worried the university would be shut down for good. The year before the legislature had discussed closing FAMU, because, they said, a black university was not needed, now that blacks could attend historically white universities. That pissed Lamarcus off.

The guys ran to The Hawk Barbershop. The Hawk was next to a black grocery and always towed black folks' cars (the few that had them) if they dared settle in the wrong spot. Crowbars smashed through the Apalachee tomahawk painted on the window. Crowbars destroyed the mirrors where people appreciated what it is like to be blond. Then, when was all was dead, fire began.

What had changed in Lamarcus? His faith. His faith in progress: gone. His faith in God: gone. His faith in America: gone. His faith in his father: gone. A young man he does not know is shot by the police. His faith in the police: never existed.

In the flames is the cross that burned on the lawn of Lamarcus's father's church, Calvary African Methodist Episcopal; in the flames are black Oldsmobiles trolling to work stuffed with faces boycotting the bus system.

So damn hot in this town all the time and then add fire, just becomes hell. Tallahassee is burning, but there's tape over Tallahassee's mouth. Tallahassee's skin on fire, piercing what connects Tallahassee's limbs to Tallahassee's brain; the strongest sensation Tallahassee has ever felt, something worse, something better, than pain; Tallahassee would not scream if Tallahassee could. Tallahassee's nervous system dismantled, Tallahassee's emotions and senses told not to return to work, Tallahassee's assets divided and liquidated by venture capital, Tallahassee's soul operationalized, outsourced, assessed, made efficient. Everyone is at home, scared shitless, watching *Talented Elephants* on their television sets.

TAMMY'S FATHER, CORN, LISTENS AS THE BLINDS he is closing smack windowsills. He and Esther have known for years the world can go to pieces on a dime, and watch it go, swirling down. A powerful person can push a button and eviscerate whole cities. Plus your own neighbor might shoot you in the back of your head because they've had a bad day, and it doesn't matter whether they are African or Japanese or your own damn child, plenty of people are crazy, and all of them are doing as they please. Oh the stories Corn heard up late smoking with Esther on the porch. Esther would bring him his after-dinner milk, cornbread, and onion, and he would dunk the cornbread and onion into the milk and read the paper which he didn't read in the morning.

After putting the kids down she'd come out to the porch. The porch'd be steamy, all the things a kitchen is plus mosquitoes and crickets galore; they'd sing into the walls of the house too; you'd get used to silence not existing, to this subtropical electric buzz. Esther would have stories just about *the drive* to work, not only work itself.

"I don't want you going up there tomorrow," says Corn to Esther.

Esther is lying on the bed, her feet in fuzzy slippers, her body loose in her nurse's dress which she sometimes wears around the house, with the giant grey sheets of the paper she is reading spread up over her head like a roof during rain. She is eating pickled pig's feet from a jar of neon red vinegar. God, he'd never thought he'd marry a woman that read newspapers instead of magazines. Sunk on the bed, her fat clumps at her waist and legs. Lord they're old.

"I don't how who'll be out tomorrow," he says, walking to the bed and laying down beside her, propping his head up with his elbow and staring into her elbow. God you couldn't be safe in your yard, on the street, in a bank, sleeping or awake, there are some sick puppies in the world. Corn knows the danger of his wife driving five days a week up to the Rockland Institute in Chattahoochee, over an hour along Highway 90. All the nuts live on the highways.

"There's people along the highway," says Esther.

"That's the problem," says Corn.

Once Esther had a flat and a kind man helped her change it. But do you really know who that man is, or why he is so kind? Who is driving along Highway 90 looking for trouble? Nothing is safe. You can't trust a soul. Their daughter, Tammy. How is she going to go to college in a world like ours? She will go straight from class to home to work to class to home to work to class to home to work, class me, Jesus, work me, Lord, how do some people get so messed up and how can we stop it, plus there were the stories out from Rockland, where, now that TB is on the decline, Esther is a nurse for the insane, bringing them jello. In an old barracks built to fight the Seminoles in the Seminole wars or what have you. Esther friendly with all the doctors, but not herself a doctor.

Corn runs a finger up Esther's leg.

DILSEY IS IN THE KITCHEN DRAPING THE mullet in sputtering oil and stirring the mullet-head soup. Dilsey aches with Tallahassee the town, her lower back, her upper back, her middle back, every little bone and piece of fat flesh in her back. If the town is a body of humans as the human body is a city of cells (as a body of water is a cistern of shells), the town mourns just as it shits, just as it laughs, just as it cries in pain or is reborn in Christ, is a midwife to the ungrateful, is sweat on cotton, water stuck around a globe. Dilsey, one with Tallahassee, limps across the kitchen like a rabid dog's been shot. Dilsey is the town and the town is Dilsey. There is Dilsey, fifteen miles wide, spread out upon the earth like Gulliver in lumpen land, strung up by the lollipop guild or the teacher's union, and the town, with all her buildings and oak trees, is squished, atomically, into this amorphous body, limping across a kitchen in a cell in one of Dilsey's organs spread out over the fields of pines, ooo-wee.

Dilsey looks down at a whole mullet took from Corn, that Dilsey will filet herself, keeping the head for soup, because Dilsey likes it like that and does it right when Corn does wrong.

Dilsey is startled by rapping on the kitchen window. Lamarcus's face is in the screen.

"Whatcha doing?" Dilsey asks through the window.

"Ya deaf?" asks Lamarcus. "There's a revolution happening."

"In here there's dinner happening," says Dilsey. "Don't be so loud."

"They shot Reverend King," he says, "Muthafuckas shot Reverend King."

"I'm working," says Dilsey. "Mr. Moody's liable to shoot you he sees your black ass hopping around like a dog. They ain't gon talk about your death on the radio all day long."

"I came to get you out of this house."

"You've come. You can leave. Did you mention to mama and daddy you're going to jail tonight?"

"They're burning a lot of the white-owned stores."

"Burn what? Who they?"

"They gon burn the same house you frying your fish in. They gonna take the Undeniable Sausage and deny it three times." He laughs.

"The Citizens Council?"

"You thick, woman. Us. We gon burn it."

Dilsey drops the mullet she is holding onto the counter. "You ain't gon burn this house. Nobody gon burn this house."

"They're already up and down the block. People are throwing stones. They burnt Hawk's barber. I can't control it."

"Go tell daddy," says Dilsey. She runs out of the kitchen across the yard to the tiny living room. In the yard she runs into Mary, who is tossing a football to herself. "My beloved," says Dilsey. "I gotta talk to your father, can you keep an eye on the stove?" *(There were always eyes on the stove.)*

"What you making?" asks Mary.

"Mullet-head soup," calls Dilsey as she steps onto the screened porch of the main house. The living room is empty. She bangs on Corn and Esther's door.

Nothing.

"Sorry," she hollers. "I got big news."

"Don't yell in the house," says Corn, opening the door halfway. He's shirtless. "Who's shot now?"

"Sorry, sir," says Dilsey.

The dark yellow blinds are closed and the tiniest trickle of dusklight comes through the blinds.

"Yes?" asks Corn.

"Mr. Moody," says Dilsey. "Lamarcus says colored folks are burning all the white-owned businesses. He's worried 'bout us."

"How by chance does he know such a thing?"

"Hawk's barber already burnt."

Corn kneels by the bed and pulls out the rifle case. "Esther, take Dilsey and the kids down to the lagoon."

"Down to the lagoon?"

"Do as I say."

"Mary and Tammy," calls Esther. "Mary, come in here now!"

"Mary's in the kitchen watching the stove," says Dilsey. "Maybe I should take the kids away. I can take em down along the gully to Smokey Hollow."

"This is not a time for your crazy ideas, Dilsey," says Corn. To Corn, Dilsey will always be a child. "You don't know what type of retribution's gon be dealt in your neighborhood tonight."

"You think they'll burn down our rentals?" asks Esther. "Maybe you should go down there and ask the Reverend and Mrs. Anderson to spend the night somewhere else."

"Preacher's family is safe," says Dilsey.

TAMMY, ELEVEN, SCRAMBLES AROUND the girls' bedroom. She cannot find her cat-rimmed glasses. She grabs her great-grandma's tablecloth and two pages of fractions.

Esther sends Dilsey for her oriental painting.

Mary's in the kitchen faithfully monitoring the stove, letting all the ruckus and commotion fade into her desire for the heat of the stove.

They are all in the backyard moving toward the lagoon.

"The specimen book," shouts Tammy. Dilsey is helping her.

"No time to get it," says Esther. They reach the lake. They hear fire, like popguns on Christmas. Corn is coming down.

"A firebomb came through the window of the front door," says Corn. "The carpet's caught. I got Elmer." He holds up the baby alligator they keep in the bathtub.

"Where's Mary?" asks Esther.

"Where the hell is Mary?" asks Corn. "I told you to get the girls out of the house."

"I got the girls out of the house," says Esther. Esther and Corn run back to the house.

THE WHOLE MULLET DILSEY WAS SET TO filet, that is lying on the counter, curls up and grips the filet knife in his little pectoral fin. The mullet has had enough! Fed up! Dropping in and dropping out. The mullet rises up on its tail and scampers across the counter to behind Mary, where Mary is leaned into the cupboard with the cookbooks, searching for the specimen book. The mullet aims the filet knife, and thrusts it into Mary's throat and deheads Mary, step one.

The mullet stares into the eyes of the stove and tosses Mary's head in a chicken-broth-filled stockpot, navy blue, swept with silver speckles like the arm of our spiral galaxy you can trace with your finger lying in the cool sands of the Gulf, engulfed with nitrogen and oxygen, orbiting a ball of burning light. The stockpot is circular and the contents change with heat like all life ever, or perhaps all death, and bubbles grow forever and disappear.

Mary's little white head—the mouth sacrificed to mouth-fill; vines of blood weaving magnetically through an onionated sea— sets off a boil the broth will spend a broth-life nurturing. The broth boils curvaceous concave convex volleyball blanket air lava hyperbole pork-ends bubbling pocks beach geometry rumbling sleep-foam epcot invert teardrop loch billowing bellowing coils-hot. In the steam Dilsey and Mary scrub burnt coconut flakes from Bundt pans. In the condensation on the metal Dilsey chases half-naked Mary after the ice-cream truck. In the heat of the water, on the boiling surface, Dilsey and Mary thread their hands along Christmas lights, searching for burnt-out bulbs.

The Christmas bulbs are the bubbles in the broth, expanding until lickety-split they pop.

THE MULLET STANDS IN THE KITCHEN, BENT over Mary's headless body.

The radio wants to hug the mullet, hug anything, but he doesn't have it in him to bend his antennae.

"Martin Luther King all gone," says the radio. "Martin Luther King kaput."

Mary's legs thrash like a fish whose tail keeps thrashing, a spasm, even after death. Her blood follows the low places across the green linoleum.

"I am lonely," says the radio.

The mullet slips out the house, down the back steps, mosies to the sea. Leaps in and feels how water feels on a face, how water, abundant, feels at home on a face after generations of dry-cracked drought.

"You listenin?" asks the radio, tryin, failin, to bend antennae.

TAMMY AND DILSEY WATCH THE WINDOW SHEENS of her parents' house melt like hot glue gun drizzles onto the soil, to dry and be scraped away by moaning fingernail machines. "I have had a good life," says Tammy. "Honey, I am going to live with a friend for a while," she says. "There are some losses you never recover from," she says.

Tammy's sons Jackson and Quentin, now fifteen and seventeen, making figure eights on their bikes, over the roots of the trees. "Listen little girl," Quentin calls to his mother,

"Come get up on my shoulders." She has not been taught enough stranger danger.

"Can I go for a ride?" she asks Dilsey.

"You got to learn not to ask other people," says Dilsey. "Men are mullet-heads. You ought to be polite, but make your own choices."

Tammy climbs onto her son Quentin's shoulders. Her moccasins, the fashion that year, dangle over his torso. Jackson and Quentin, with Tammy on Quentin's shoulders, bicycle west for days and nights without sleeping without talking without singing along Highway 90 now-dead with her county-courthouse mausoleums. They turn a sharp right and are in Selma near Corn's childhood farm in Autaugaville where Corn was whipped ten hours a day by a widowed dad before heading off for Camp Gordon Johnston, then Normandy.

Tammy and her sons Jackson and Quentin stand on the Edmund Pettus Bridge in Selma where on March 9, 1965, the Reverend Dr. Martin Luther King, Jr., led across marchers who two days before had been beaten back, marchers who petitioned for a court injunction and said, We shall not again be beaten back, and Jackson and Quentin ask their mother, would you like to play Pooh Sticks off the Edmund Pettus Bridge just like you will one day teach me to play off the little bridge over the creek in Myers Park where De Soto spent the first Christmas in the United States, in Anhaica, the most important town of the Apalachee, the people that used to live on the banks of the creek with the little bridge in Myers Park where we will learn to play Pooh Sticks without ever having learned about them? Could we play Pooh Sticks, the game you have never told us was taught to you and your dead sister by your black nanny?

Tammy says, "Let's do it." They go to the banks of the river for sturdy twigs and they drop their twigs off the bridge to see, just like Winnie the Pooh, whose stick floats out first from under the other side of the bridge.

"I am going to do two jobs in my life," says Tammy, looking up to Jackson and Quentin. "I am going to work three decades at Corn Palace, serving breakfast, and I am going to raise you into whole, happy beings."

THE APALACHEE RIVER HAS TATTOOS. THE RIVER wears a tight shirt the hulking middrift of the river flowing, the river's boxers scrunched on the ryverbyanks, the boxers clodded and melted against the bank where the turtles soak in the sun even when the sun is shy by the semen-glob clouds that fling from the paper-towel encrusted hand of the river that loves itself and knows that it is safe in the arms of the cypress trees, which, having been thrown, through geologic time, in and out of the slammer, have friends on both banks of the law. The river has its trendy bag that matches its sand-green jeans that is filled with pebbles and baby alligators and lip gloss in shiny aluminum sticks, aluminum sticks covered in pebble dust wet by alligator tears.

The spring pumps iron and other minerals. The water gushes and gushes from a hole in the earth. It gurgles up and bursts forth and, like the clear juice of a cool cauldron overflowing, runs to the green banks and soothes them and feels them and frees them and asks the banks, do you want happy endings, and when the banks deny them in their proud matted dryness the water ebbs and returns into itself. The water curls, an actress, near the mouth of the spring, but the water looks like nothing, like a bottle without plastic. A fedora of green branches is worn by the spring (and what that means). The timeless spring the spring cut off completely from our human times and needs and foibles (as if we couldn't spring without it! as if we are somehow separate!). The spring that never dies and never gets sent to timeout because it is out of time and one thing, although innately unstably patterned like aluminum foil and the light from the sun on the water like light on aluminum foil, the Earth an aluminum stick covered in pebble dust wet by alligator tears.

The rain is coming, the rain is coming, we're going to get hammered. The hammers come, mallets, are those the feathers of mallard ducks on the wind, with malleable royal blue circles? and shucks the heather of the hammers in the ether to come beat here. Rubber hammers, flimsy rubber hammers raining down, drumming, ramming, drama is dancing, and our bodies, the ricochets of the hammers on bodies. We pour shaking drinks into shaking clinks we are getting hammered getting hammered getting hammered. We watch the big grey thing pass across the flat water we are big flat grey things full of water gushes and gushes the sail the candle.

JOHN MORAN

Friday

From the old bridge
devout Muslim men
capped in God's entwinement
watch the dredging for the new bridge, drawn,
as I, to metallic pounds.

Friday. Praise Allah and liquor.
Young men are giving free motorcycle rides
to lost queers.
Cricket pickups are chemically expanding
quicker than this tree
knocking open the sidewalk.

Arrangements

an arrangement: littered egg shells bright white

a monument: temple banyan tree bright red

an arrangement: white bird shit fading on the honeycomb
bricks

a monument: black human shit drying in the grooves

an arrangement: shit-and-crow-topped baby-blue buses beneath
banyans

a monument: rotting crimpled plastic

a monument: my boogers coal-black on my callused index

an arrangement: particulate matter

an arrangement: paw print pattern of joyful skipping of three-
legged stray dog

a monument: dirt on the smashed cigarette pack in the shadow
of the inoperable septic clad in dust vines in the shadow of
the hammering half-baked flyover which has covered the
immediate stray jungle in purple-grey ash

an arrangement: all the stray dogs on this bridge are twins
because they were weaned by the same sloshing tits of the
bitch who bore

One Mistake

One mistake was
listening to my body.
Another was believing
human connection can
be kept over time.
None of us talks to
each other because we
worry the other
person might be uncool
and we might become
contaminated.
The roof of this
public building is like
the pentagon the
employee is sanitizing
his hands the Indian
American is plugged
into the outlet between
the vending machines
here comes the random
mass shooter.
What had been good
about this place
was the absence of
white people and
their loud haughty
presence and their
excessive baggage. I
had sat by a man

who looked not good
in not good clothes,
to prove my anti-racism
because he was
black and he sneezed
like he had
tuberculosis and some
man who gave me
head recently snorted
some chemical before
and my phone will
die in my pocket while
I am the victim of
the mass shooter
here beneath the
cement pantheon
we will be separated
from the poems we are
addicted too. Sorry,
I meant phones. We
will be separated
from the poems we are
addicted to. Phones.

Complicated Republican

Once I knew a Republican
who played the didgeridoo
he juggled, too
grew lichens recreationally
due to extensive botanical knowledge
rolled sushi at home
due to cosmopolitan openness
served meals at the shelter
due to fiery Catholicism
he was a die-hard Republican
with gay friends
a pick-up truck
a cowboy hat
a Polish grandmother
a love of history
a tickled laugh
a permit to hunt gators
a hatred of a woman's right to choose
he was pretty tan
he was against real estate development
in wetlands and swamps and all places holy
he juggled fire
he taught himself Quechua
imagine that
a Republican speaking Quechua

SERHIY ZHADAN

TRANSLATED BY REILLY COSTIGAN-HUMES
AND ISAAC STACKHOUSE WHEELER

Voroshilovgrad

Wheat fields surrounded the airport. Some bright, poisonous looking flowers were growing closer to the runway. Wasps were hovering lazily above, frozen in mid-flight as if there were corpses below them. Every morning the sun heated up the asphalt and dried out all the grass poking through the concrete slabs. Flags were whipping in the wind off to the side, above the air-traffic control station. A bit farther away, behind the administration building, the blistering morning sun touched down on a row of trees woven together by spiderwebs. Strange gusts of wind tore across the fields like animals emerging from the night, attracted by the airport's green lights, only to retreat back into the wheat to hide from the burning June sun. As it warmed up, the asphalt reflected the sunlight, blinding the birds flying over the runway. Gas tanks and a couple of trucks were parked at the fence. Some empty garages, smelling of sweet stagnant water and oil, were just emerging from the darkness. After a while, some mechanics appeared, changed into worn black overalls, and started fiddling around with their machines. The early June sky hovered above the airport, flapping loudly in the wind like freshly washed sheets, rising and swooping down to the asphalt. Around eight, the laborious roar of an engine made itself heard, heaving air in and out of the depths of the atmosphere. The airplane itself was still hidden behind the sun, but its shadow scurried across the wheat fields, scaring the hell out of the birds and foxes. The surface of the sky shattered like porcelain. A good old Antonov An-2, the pride of Soviet aviation, a model that had seen its share of combat, though this one was almost certainly a crop duster, was descending nearby. Deafening the morning with its prehistoric motor, it spun around the sleepy city, awakening its residents from their light and fleeting summer dreams. The pilots scoped out the fields of crops topped with sunny honey, fresh grass sprouting on the railroad ties and embankments, the golden river sand, and the chalky banks the color of silverware. The city was left behind with its factory smoke stacks and railroad; the airplane was getting ready to land. Light poured into the cockpit and shone coldly on the metal. The machine whipped across the runway, its stiff wheels bouncing up and down on the cracked asphalt. The pilots hopped down onto the ground and started helping the baggage handlers pull out large burlap sacks full of regional and Republic-wide newspapers, letters, and parcels. Once everything had been unloaded, they walked over to the building, leaving the plane to warm up in the sun.

My friends and I lived on the other side of the fields, on the outskirts of the city, in white panel apartment buildings surrounded by tall pine trees. In the evenings, we would escape from our neighborhood, roam around in the wheat, hiding from passing cars and scampering along the fence, and then we'd take a rest in the dusty grass and look at the aircraft. The An-2, with its all-metal airframe and canvas-upholstered wings, looked like something not of this world, some conveyance utilized by demons who burned the sky above us with oil and lead. God's messengers were riding inside it; the mighty propeller was smashing the blue ice of the sky and hurling poplar fuzz into the next world. We came home well after dark, pushing through the hot, thick wheat, all the while dreaming about aviation. We all wanted to become pilots. The majority of us became losers.

From time to time I still have dreams about aviators. They're always making an emergency landing somewhere in wheat fields. Their planes cut at dusk through the thick wheat like razors; all the canvas upholstery gives with a loud ripping sound as the stalks wrap around their planes' undercarriages before they become bogged down forever in the black, dried-up earth. The pilots bail out of their boiling cockpits and fall into the wheat that immediately spins a web around their legs. They stand and peer into the distance as if they're trying to make out something on the horizon. But there's nothing on the horizon except for more wheat fields. They go on for miles; there's no hope of reaching the end. The aviators leave their aircraft to cool down in the twilight and make their way west, chasing the rapidly guttering sun. The stalks are tall and impassable; the pilots can hardly make their way through the fields; they forge along nonetheless and smash up against an invisible wall, over and over again, even though they know they have no chance of getting out. They're wearing leather helmets, goggles, flight gloves. For some reason, they don't want to detach their open parachutes; they trail the aviators like long and heavy crocodile tails.

WHEN EVENING CAME TO THE GAS STATION, the mechanic, an improbably rotund former striker named Injured, gave the rest of us a mute farewell and went home. Kocha, the attendant, was still sitting on his favored contraption—two detached car seats covered with the black skins of some unidentifiable animals, with a long metal arm or lever attached to one of the seats, making the thing look like a catapult. He seemed to have gotten stuck in some sort of odd torpor; neither Injured's departure nor the various passing truck drivers' repeated requests that he fill up their tanks made the least impression on him. Injured had shown me how to work the pumps, so I was the one who waited on the three larger-than-life tractor-trailers that came by, looking like huge, weary lizards. The sun had floated over to the other side of the highway, and the twilight burst open like a sunflower. Kocha came to life just as the evening did. Around nine he stood up, locked the booth, and wandered listlessly over to the far edge of the lot. With a heavy sigh, he looped around the truck cab I had slept in last night, squeezed himself inside, and sprawled out in the driver's seat, extending his legs through the shattered window. I crawled in after him and sat in the passenger seat. Down below, darkness was enveloping the valley. To the east, the sky was already covered in a dim haze, while to the west, right above our heads, red flames spilled across the whole valley, heralding the arrival of night. Mist rose off the river, concealing the little silhouettes of fishermen and the surrounding houses, rolling out onto the road and drifting into the suburbs. The fog that hovered over the valley the city sat in was white. The valley was fading away into darkness, growing more and more indistinct, until it resembled a riverbed, though up here, in the hills, it was still light. Kocha, wide-eyed and stupefied, was staring down at it all, unblinking, his gaze fixed on the advancing night.

"Here," I said, handing Kocha my MP3 player.

He put the earphones on over his balding head, tapping some buttons to adjust the volume.

"What is this, anyway?" he asked.

"Charlie Parker. I ripped ten CDs' worth."

Kocha listened for a bit, and then put the 'phones down, off to the side.

"You know why I like it out here?" I asked him. "There aren't any airplanes going by."

He looked up. It was true; there really weren't any planes. There were still some lights, though: just reflections, maybe, shooting across the sky; green sparks glowing here and there; golden balls spinning along; clouds massing to the north, giving off little sparkles.

"But there are always satellites up there," Kocha answered finally. "You can see them very well at night. When I'm not sleeping I always see them."

"And why aren't you sleeping, old-timer?"

"Well," Kocha said, every consonant still coming out with a screech, "the thing is, I've got sleeping troubles. Ever since the army, Herman. You know how it goes in the paratroopers—those drops, the adrenaline... it sticks with you, for life."

"Gotcha."

"So I bought some sleeping pills. I asked for something that would really knock my socks off. They gave me some kind of weird artificial shit. God knows what they're putting in pills these days. Anyway, I started taking it, but it didn't do a thing. I upped the dose and I still couldn't fall asleep. Thing is, though, I've started sleeping during the day now. It's a real head-scratcher..."

"What have you been taking?" I asked him. "Can I have a look?"

Kocha rooted through his overall pockets and took out a bottle; the label was a poisonous-looking green. I took the bottle and tried reading it, but I didn't even recognize the characters on it.

"Maybe it's some sort of cockroach repellent. Who even makes these pills?"

"They told me the French do."

"But look at these hieroglyphs—does that look like French to you? Okay, okay—how about I try one?"

I twisted off the cap, took out a lilac-colored pill, and popped it into my mouth.

"Nah, man," Kocha said, taking back the bottle. "If you only take one you won't even feel it. I take at least five."

Kocha dumped a few pills down his throat, as if to validate this statement.

"Gimme that." I took the bottle back, poured out a few pills, and downed them. Then I just sat there, trying to focus in on my own sensations, waiting for the pills to kick in.

"Kocha, it doesn't feel like they're doing anything."

"I told you so."

"Maybe you need to wash them down."

"I tried doing that … with wine."

"And?"

"Nothing. My piss just turned red."

The twilight thickened, slipping through the tree branches and reaching out into the warm, dusty grass wrapping around us. Flaming orange balls hung in the valley, their sharp citrusy light burning through the fog. The sky was turning black and distant, the constellations showing through like a face appearing on a negative. But the night's most salient feature was the fact that I didn't have the slightest desire to sleep. Kocha put on my headphones again and began swaying softly to an inaudible beat.

Then I noticed movement somewhere down below. Someone was coming up from the river, ascending the steep slope. The hillside was buried in fog; I couldn't make anything out, but it sounded as though somebody was herding skittish animals away from the water.

"You see that?" I asked Kocha warily.

"Yep, I sure do," Kocha replied, nodding happily.

"Who's down there?"

"Yeah, yeah," Kocha said, continuing to nod, contemplating the night that had pounced on us so suddenly.

I froze, listening hard to the voices that were becoming more distinct as whoever it was drew nearer in the darkness that clung to everything like some thick, acerbic liquid. Lit by the valley below, the fog now seemed full of motion and shadows. I could see into the space above it, where some bats occasionally whipped by, making circles above our heads then abruptly darting back into the wet haze. The voices got louder, the rustling resolved into individual footsteps, and then, all at once, bodies started swimming out of the fog, gliding quickly across the thick, hot grass toward us. They moved easily up the slope—there were more and more of them. I could already see the first ones' faces;

new, distinct voices carried out of the fog now, and they sounded sweet and sharp as they soared into the sky like smoke from fireplaces. When the first ones drew even with me, I wanted to call something out, something that would stop them, but I was at a loss for words. I could only sit there and observe them silently as they came nearly face-to-face with us, only to push on, not stopping or paying any attention to us, disappearing back into the nighttime haze. I couldn't understand what kind of creatures they were; they were strange, nearly formless; men with clumps of fog tucked away in their lungs. They were tall, with long, unkempt hair that they had pulled back into ponytails or else wore in Mohawks. Their faces were dark and scarred; some of them had odd painted signs and letters on their foreheads, while others had piercings in their ears or noses. Some of them had covered their faces with bandanas. Medallions and binoculars dangled from their necks, and they had fishing poles and guns slung over their shoulders. One was holding a flag, while another carried a long dry stick with a dog's head on the end. Somebody was carrying a cross, and somebody else seemed to be carrying all his belongings in a bundle. Many of them had drums; they weren't beating them, however; they were hoisted over their shoulders. The creatures' clothing was striking but bedraggled—somebody was wearing an officer's jacket, while others were decked out in sheepskins. Many were wearing long, simple white garments dotted with cow's blood. One of them wasn't wearing a shirt, and his extensive tattoos gave off a blue light under the glowing stars. Another one was wearing army boots, while somebody else had laced sandals on, though most walked along barefoot, crushing bugs and field mice and stepping on thorns, although they showed no signs of discomfort. Women, whispering back and forth in the dark, and occasionally bursting into laughter, followed the men. Some wore their hair in buns, and many of them had dreads, but the pack even included some bald ladies, their skulls painted red and blue. Icons and pentagrams hung from their necks, and they were carrying drowsy and hungry children on their shoulders, children whose eyes soaked up the darkness around them. The women's dresses were long and colorful; it looked as though they had been wrapped in the flags of some unknown republics. They wore bracelets and baubles around their ankles, and one of them even had little silver rings on her toes. After they too had passed, more dark figures began to burst out of the fog, one by one. They were like nothing I had ever seen before. Some had rams' horns on their heads wrapped in ribbons and golden paper, while other figures were covered in thick fur. Yet another group followed after them, with turkey feathers rustling behind their backs, while the last cohort, the darkest and least talkative, were deformed, each looking as though they'd been created by merging two bodies together— they walked along with two heads on their shoulders, two hearts in their chests, and enough life in them to die twice. Then weary cow heads poked out of the fog; it was unclear how this strange tribe had forced their animals to climb the steep hill, but there they were, plodding along, dragging harrows bearing blind snakes and dead fighting dogs. The harrows erased the tracks left by the incredible procession that had just passed us. Then we saw that the cows were being goaded on by herders in black and grey overcoats. They were moving the animals through the night, taking great pains not to leave any tracks behind. I recognized a few of the herders' faces—the only problem being that I couldn't remember where I'd seen them before. They noticed me too, but they simply looked me right in the eyes, forcing me to give up any last semblance of composure before they pushed on, leaving behind a scorched smell of iron and burning skin. The sky had already started to turn white over wherever they'd come from. As soon as they disappeared, the air was injected with an even, grey light, the new morning filling it up like water poured into a vessel. A red crack ran across the sky, and morning sunlight doused the valley. Kocha was still sitting next to me—he seemed to be sleeping...with his eyes open. I sucked in a sharp breath through my nose. Morning did come, but a bitter aftertaste of the voices that had been there a moment ago remained in the air. It felt as though death or a freight train had just come through.

AS THE DAY WORE ON, KOCHA AND Injured sat soaking up the sun, sitting in the chairs by the booth. Kocha had unbuttoned his overalls down to his chest; he sat there tanning a body as withered and pale as some dusty relic. Injured was wearing a foppish snow-white dress shirt, meticulously ironed black pants, and polished, pointed shoes. He looked like a farmer who was marrying off his only daughter. Suddenly a leather ball flew out through the open garage doors—it landed heavily and rolled down the warm macadam. Injured stepped up to the ball, chipped it up with his polished shoe, moving pretty easily for a guy his weight, popped it into the air, and started juggling just as easily with his left foot. His movements were easy and effortless; he sucked in his stomach adeptly so the ball wouldn't hit it as he kept it afloat, occasionally heading it or tapping it with his shoulder. Kocha and I froze, observing these miracles of motion. Injured still had it—he'd hardly even broken a sweat, though his eyes were a bit red from exertion and his breathing slightly labored. And there was his stomach, twisting and turning and always seeming to get in the way, despite his best efforts.

Three trucks pulled in off the highway as the performance continued. The drivers hurried over, greeted Kocha, and joined in watching Injured.

"Injured!" one of them yelled, clearly dying to play. "Pass!"

Injured glanced at him, and kicked the ball in his direction. The driver stepped on it, took one slightly awkward touch, and booted it as hard as he could back to Injured. Injured trapped it and then clamped it between his legs. The drivers could no longer contain themselves, and they all bolted toward him, howling like wild animals. It was on. Injured spun away from the drivers' embraces and did circles around his opponents, forcing them to fall and trip over each other—holding onto the ball all the while. The drivers were charging at Injured like dogs going after a sleepy bear, but they were utterly hopeless. They started smacking each other in frustration, clearly trying to assign blame. Injured was starting to get short of breath, so he dropped far back on the macadam strip. He'd been kicked in the shins a few times and now was limping a bit. Smelling blood, the drivers pressed their attack with fresh vigor. Injured faked out one of them out, causing him to ram his head into his teammate; both dropped to the asphalt like bowling pins. The third driver ran over to help them up. Injured caught his breath and looked over in our direction.

"Herman," he yelled, "get in here—it's three against one, ya know..."

I dashed over onto the strip. Injured passed the ball to me; I took possession and carried it across the "field." The drivers too were running out of steam after circling a few times, so they stopped, rested their hands on their knees, and tried catching their breath. Their tongues lolled like the tongues of corpses, or tickets poking out of trolley machines. I stopped, waiting for a response from Injured. He motioned toward the drivers, as if to say, "Let them play a bit." I booted the ball to the tallest guy; he was standing the closest to me. Elated, he dashed for the ball, turned around, and hammered the leather sphere as hard as he could. The ball shot into the sky, slicing through the air and seemingly brushing against the clouds before disappearing into the grass behind the macadam strip. The drivers' spirits were nearly broken, but after a brief team meeting, they decided to venture off into the thicket. Injured and I followed them.

Even Kocha got up. We moved into the dust and enveloping warmth like African hunters trying to lure lions into the open. The ball was sitting somewhere in the brush; you could hear its muffled growling, its faintly beating leather heart. We advanced cautiously, trying to catch a glimpse of it—occasionally we'd call out to each other and have a look at the sky, where more and more clouds kept rolling in.

It all reminded me of something—men wading warily through waist-high grass, pushing the blades back, gazing fixedly at the texture of the plants around them, listening to the sounds coming out of the brush, goading skittish animals out of the foliage, slowly crossing an unending field. I'd seen this before. Tense backs, silhouettes standing still in the twilight, white dress shirts shining in the darkness.

When had I seen it before? Back in 1990, I think. Yeah, 1990. In the summer. We'd just won a home game against Voroshilovgrad. Injured scored late in the match. It may have been his best game ever. We were at a restaurant called Ukraine, over by the park, across from the fire station. It was evening, and we were celebrating the victory: our players as well as local gangsters, women wearing fancy dresses and men wearing white dress shirts or track suits, waiters—budding capitalists, all of us, sitting together with all kinds of crooks, hot waves of alcohol breaking over our heads. It made me think of when we'd dare each other to run into the sea at night: a bittersweet, black wave washes over you and then you run back out onto the beach, no longer a boy, but a man. Boxes of vodka; an endless table seating everyone you know; loud, crappy music; blue, damp twilight shining in through the window; drenched trees; voices blending together and reminding you of the rain; men and women talking, the overwhelming feeling of approaching some precipice with hot, unbearable drafts rising from beyond to take your breath away and make your pupils dilate, the underlying sensation of invisible vessels pumping the whole world's blood. Suddenly, there's the sound of shattering glass amid all that golden shimmering, and the air burst into a million crystal pieces—some Voroshilovgrad fan had tracked us down, and he threw a brick through the restaurant window. The dark blue night poured into the room, chilling our blood and knocking our spinning heads back into sobriety. Next came a short silence, followed by general movement, angry voices, everyone suddenly bursting with courage, loud shuffling through the doors, more broken glass, the stomping of shoes on the wet asphalt, white dress shirts standing out sharply as men sprang into the lilac-colored night, female silhouettes by the window peering anxiously into the darkness. Gangsters and capitalists, soccer players and the neighborhood crew—all of them spilling out through the darkness and combing the wasteland beyond the park, chasing their invisible quarry toward the river, refusing to let it get away; an odd pursuit full of excitement and joy—nobody wants to fall behind, everyone stares into the overwhelming darkness of the summer, ducking around and trying to catch a glimpse of the enemy. Distant electric lights burn beyond the river as if yellow-green suns are burying themselves in the grass; we want to lure them out, so they can dissolve the surrounding darkness—it's thickening like blood, hot blood shot into an internal combustion engine by the effort of our breathing.

KOCHA SLEPT SOUNDLY THAT NIGHT, AS IF he wasn't dreaming but just lying there while someone herded dreams through his mind. They rolled through him like trains passing a junction, and he inspected each of them as though he were the station manager, focused and earnest. I lugged an old overcoat out of the trailer and draped it over him. I also got up a few times during the night and went over to check up on him. The stray dogs that had been roaming the lot slept at his feet, and the wind pushed paper bags along the macadam strip. Birds sat on Kocha's shoulders and while ants crawled up onto his open palms, licking off the blue and orange dust. The last of the clouds rolled off to the north, and constellations spread out across the sky. It was starting to feel like June again. June was always fleeting and eventful around here—stems would fill up with slightly bitter juice and leaves would turn rough like skin exposed to the cold. Each passing day meant more dust and sand—it got in our shoes and the creases of our clothing, grated in our teeth, and rained from our hair. In June, the air would heat up like army tents, kicking off the season of sluggish men in the streets and rowdy kids in streams. It was already clear by morning that we should be bracing ourselves for a merciless summer that might continue until the end of time and scorch everything in its wake, including our skin and hair. Not even the rain would give us any relief.

ANTHONY MADRID

Pants Pants Pants

Pants, pants, pants!
And we're bouncin' off the walls
And Peter Rich'll teach ya which
Ya beach- and basketballs

Ya beach- and basketballs
Ya slam 'em in the net
HELL sinky! kinda kinky
Key to *Oubliette*

Umma-gumma yes, ma'am
Oh m'God, no
There's the siren, Keats and Byron
Tie! it's time to go

Guy, it's time to go!
'Cuz we're bouncin' off the walls
Like a rimshot Abbottabad
Ya beach- and basketballs

Ya kitchykitchy coo
Ya got a lot to do
And Bone-a-beck and Schoonebeek
Have found the fella who,

With a Walla Walla weedwhack
Whack-a-mole stick, said:
"You're a goner, Weimaraner."
Stop! I'm getting sick!

Ticklebug, Ticklebug
Quotin' up a storm
And Lollygag and Pantyhose
Are kinda getting warm

With a tabbernack, grabbernack
Tabulate the bill
They try to give Manhattan back
To Crackerjack and Jill

Boutonnière, boutonnière!
Buddha bourguignon
And the Taliban and Yes-We-Can
'll tell ya whatcha won

While the Wannabe and Wonton
Are walking on the bridge
They took a little jaunt on
The way to gettin' rich

Like an ixodid, ixodid,
Ixodid tick • Rocky
Mountain spotted fever with a
-pherson and a Mac-

On your mark get set you're dead
Arizona Schoonebeek
'Cuz the powderpuff has had enough
Of pounding on ya neck

And the Maki babe, khaki babe
'll pile 'em up and, oh!
The baby gotta incubate
Vagina dynamo

Aw c'mon, it's time to go!
With the chicken and the chicks
And the clock, clock, clock
And ya tockin' to the ticks

Like a pants, pants, pants
Let it echo down the halls
'Cuz we're getting in the barrel
Gonna reckon with the Falls

Gonna reckon with Niagara
Gonna kick it in the balls
Singing PANTS PANTS PANTS
While we're bouncing off the walls

Four Four Four

Four, four, four
There's a dolphin on the floor
And a little jellybean
And a Delly-delly-phine

And a camisole Camille
When the camels start to squeal
When you're four, four, four
Who could ask for any more?

Quarter mile, quarter mile
Howdja like me now and how's ya
Bibbinism, Bibbinism?
Miaow, miaow, miaow

This disturbin' university
And bourbon ingenue
With a Bibbinism, Bibbinism
You, you, you

But the Galahad, Galahad
He gotta get a job • I'm
Coming from la Mancha, cantcha
See the demagogue

Cantcha see the Commie Tommy gun
Is toppin' off ya tank
And the Wangbang and Nackanack
Have no one left to thank

And then they stack it up, back it up
And jackin' up the car • they are
Often soften-coughin'
All the way to Zanzibar

With a marzipan orangutan
A Mangapwani zoo
And the Sultanate insulting it
Interpret as you do

And the Kachyderm, Pachyderm
'll pat 'em on the back
'Cuz they runnin' up the credit card
A cricket on the track

And the Clabber Girl, Clabber Girl
'll clap 'em all in chains
Like a flak-jacket, try-to-crack-it
Buddha for your pains

Puppeteer, Puppeteer!
Pop him in the nut
'Cuz the Galahad is half as bad
As only knowing what

's gonna rope-a-dope, rope-a-dope
Dopin' up the shop
'Cuz the Baine damage got a package
From Corina Copp

Collie-collie, wiener dog
And cudgel up a cake
And a nine-and-twenty blackbird
Bobbin' on the lake

With an address! address!
Lolly gag amend! • Ya gotta
Gimme 'cuz the Post Office
Won't know where to send

And then the Winnemac, Winnemac
Waiting on a train • Ya gotta
Steam it open, ibuprofen!
Take away the pain

And then the coelacanth, coelacanth
Is sealing up the crack
And the catamaran | on top o' the man
Has nobody left to thank

Just like a tuna leg and Armantrout
And RAH RAH RAH • we are
Learning how to talk about
The AH HA HA

Try Never

Last thing in the book. I trembled and shook.
A half hour down and a half hour do.
Sapphire, sapphire, I don't know who,—
And when will I ever do that again?

Try never. Try this is the end. This is
The thing they don't know about magic. It's
Just not in its nature to work every time;
If it worked every time, it'd be physics.

Try never. Try wasn't and isn't. Try to
Broker my wisdom and teacher the young.
For I have passed too many years among
Cool, designing beings.

Try never to Wallace Stevens—
That birch, that hazel, that straight, slender rowan.
The raison d'être of every kōan
Is to make you stupid for a minute.

Try rack and pinion and pivot. Reflect
That the CHILD does well, the first day she ignores
The bee's black tongue and its bomb bay doors,—
Like the nib of a retractable pen.

Hi hen, eleni y ganet. What
Comes in through the window goes out through the pipes.
And so what, if he can only be moved by stripes,
That Punchinello in a china shop—?

Try never. *Īśvaro veda.* The water
Is making its way to the drain. River
Got no shadow. River move.
The bowshot arrow has something to prove,
But I'm revoking anger's privileges.

Try never, for all your due diligence.
Try ulna resected and bystander lung.
You'll have no choice but go down among
The armless, the legless, the blind and insane.

Try never will Oliver be the same!
Try cancer and gemini, fishgoat and child.
(It's what happens when the imagination runs wild
In people with no imagination.)

Try never. Try fools always fulsome. Try
Instructive prig with her hand on a spadix.
We observe that her self-approval ratings
Are permanently sky-high.

Try never. Try I don't know why.
Try *There was nothing to see and I saw it all.*
Get a load of the plummeting waterfall—it's when
Water itself goes for a swim.

Try her and him. Try antonym.
Volcanic dust! why can't I just
Say the deal is you have a kid
And then there's all this stuff you can't talk about…

Try never. Try lifting the shot put. Try
The goddess is motionless, set to begin.
The "acorn of light" in what ought to have been
The last of Ezra Pound's *Cantos*.

Try splitting the nucleus of human vice:
Entitlement, hysteria, team spirit.
Above all, shallowness. Above all, I fear it
Will last as long as the Internet.

Try no way out. Try glass of water. Going
To their house is like becoming their daughter.
Why should gravity work? And why orbits? And why
Must I sit through my own performance?

Try the sound of exploding Christmas ornaments,
The scream of the author's circular saw.
I believe, if it wasn't against the law, you'd make me
The happiest little girl in Wyoming.

Try never. Try foaming horse with swords
And friendly hearts and Icelandic names.
I shall forever be lapped by the orange flames
Of my self-inflicted glory…

But whoever reads these sayings of mine
And teaches others to read them
Is freed from all sins, is freed from doubt,
Will give others the gift of this freedom,—

Yeah, try never. The charm's wound up.
The top of the tree is the end of the climb.
Now Do What I Say and *The Warrant for Rhyme*
Have done what they could and, one last time,
I say to you all, in a whisper: Try never.

MARIN BUSCHEL

Quiz Night Champion

THE PORTUGUESE BAKERY

Never mind that I was lying naked on a dewy lawn with a bloody harpoon set on a diagonal across my chest and no clue as to how I'd gotten there. The ranch-style house looked familiar, so I went inside, found a wallet on a catchall and matched the picture on the driver's license to the face in the bathroom mirror. It took four cups of coffee before I remembered I was the pastry chef at The Portuguese Bakery and about an hour sitting on the front porch listening to birds chirp before I felt well enough to drive there. "Can I help you?" a Czech or Slovakian or Russian girl asked as I slipped into the kitchen. "As a matter of fact you can," I said and grabbed an apron. "Pass me that...cylindrical wooden utensil." "You mean the rolling pin?" the Czech or Slovakian or Russian girl asked. "Yes, the rolling pin," I said and leaned against an enormous chrome machine. "Is this new?" "You can't be back here," another Eastern European girl said. "But I'm the pastry chef," I said as I slid to the floor. "Are you okay?" yet another Eastern European asked; this one was a guy. "Why aren't any of you Portuguese?" I asked. The guy dragged me across the kitchen floor toward a rear exit and a bustling street. "What are you doing down there?" a familiar face asked. "Just resting," I said and sat up. "What's your name again?" "You're kidding right?" the familiar face asked. "Darren Wrath. Did you hear about the captain?" "I don't think so," I said and got to my feet. "He's alive," Darren Wrath said. "It was all a hoax to torture his wife. The funeral, the death certificate, all of it. He found out she's been fucking the Quiz Night Champion."

"Who's the Quiz Night Champion?" I asked. "Good one," Darren said and went on his way. I was standing on the edge of a wharf thinking about a harpoon when I spotted a guy in a captain's hat.

THE TRANSPARENT SAILBOAT

The captain came over and shook my hand. He asked how I was holding up; I told him well enough and that I was glad he was on this side of the grass. "Thanks a bunch," he said and gave me two thumbs up. "It just so happens I've had a very productive couple of weeks in The Great Beyond. Right before your eyes, or strike me dead, is the world's very first transparent sailboat." "The world's what?" I asked. "You heard," the captain said. "It's a seventy-foot schooner with state-of-the-art engineering and room enough for thirty-some tourists. A money maker, if ever there was one." "I'm sure it'll be a hit," I said. "You don't need to tell me," the captain said. "Even the atheist wants to walk on water like The Big Man, hallowed be His name." He pointed to an empty slip. "Oh, I see," I said and took a step back. "You almost had me." "What do you mean?" the captain asked and took hold of my arm. "A captain doesn't go around doling out comeuppances to people who haven't earned them. The Missus had it coming. We both know that." "All the same," I said. "All the same nothing," the captain said as he lead me toward the empty slip. "Jump on." He nudged me just enough I lost my balance and fell off the dock; I landed on my feet, on the boat, or else on air. "Oh ye of little faith," the captain said. "I can't even see a reflection," I said as the water moved beneath my feet. "The miracles of bulletproof glass," the captain said. "Take a stroll. You're standing on the stern. The bow is to your right. Plenty of space to pace." I started for the bow, careful at first, then with more confidence. But the next step wasn't there. "Quiz Night Champion my ass," the captain said and slapped his thigh. "You're so smart, why'd you just walk the gang plank? What's that? Nope, still didn't get it. Oh, you're killing me. Try taking the water out of your mouth."

YOU'RE LIKE THAT TREE

There was a rope ladder tied off to a piling; the captain helped me onto the dock. "I'm sorry," he said and rustled my hair. "I got carried away. Give me a second to regroup." "It's okay," I said and squeezed some water from my T-shirt. "All you did was serve just desserts, right? The Czechs at The Portuguese Bakery do the same thing all day every day." "I don't think you know what just desserts are," the captain said. "But either way, you didn't deserve it. In the final analysis, none of this has been your fault." "How do you figure?" I asked. "They say I fall into shit," the captain said, "and come out smelling like roses. It isn't true. I'm shit, and that's how I smell." "You don't," I said and patted his shoulder. "You're not, I'm sure of it." "Don't touch," the captain said and raised a fist. "Nobody touches the captain." I could still hear him cursing as I headed down the wharf and across the parking lot; I didn't know what a Quiz Night Champion did with his time off, so I drove around until the gaslight lit, found a filling station, and went back to the ranch house. I'd just pulled a pillow over my head and was about to begin a dream when the phone rang. "Listen, about earlier," the captain said. "Really, you needn't," I said. "No, I want to explain," the captain said and began to tell me about a kid who got lost in the woods. He'd meant to make a pass through a stand of secondary growth toward a river but got distracted by a doe and tracked her for over an hour before discovering he had no idea where he was. "The kid just lost it," the captain said. "He beat the crap out of the first tree he saw." "Sounds painful," I said. "You're like that tree," the captain said. "You're not the Quiz Night Champion." "I'm not?" I asked. "No," he said. "You're innocent." "Thank you," I said and passed the phone to the woman in my bed. "Who was it?" she asked, returning the receiver to its cradle. "It was your husband," I said. "Go back to sleep."

QUIZ NIGHT

"My husband?" the captain's wife asked and clicked the bedside lamp. "But that's impossible. The captain's dead." "I'm afraid not," I said. "It was all a hoax. The funeral, the death certificate. I thought you knew. I thought everybody knew. And I thought I was the Quiz Night Champion." "You, the Quiz Night Champion?" the captain's wife asked and covered her mouth. "I need to get home. Widow or no, this was a horrible idea." "Maybe," I said, "but we're in it together, right?" The captain's wife dressed and left. I went downstairs, poured myself a glass of milk, and sat in the dark with my face in my hands. Not only had I been ditched by a beautiful woman in the middle of the night, I'd been demoted from Quiz Night Champion— and that was just since midnight. Earlier, I'd invited a married woman over for cocktails, answered the door in my birthday suit, and gotten all up on her. And that was just today; I still didn't know what was up with the bloody harpoon. I sat at the kitchen table, afraid to find out what I'd do next, until the following dusk when a ringing phone startled me to the floor. "Darren Wrath here," a familiar voice said. "Quiz Night at The Portuguese Bakery." "I'm there," I said and sprinted across the front lawn. Having doubled back to hang up the phone,

I floored it. "Tonight's my night," Darren said and ordered a round for the packed house. "German philosophy is my jam." A thin gentleman with a mustache and fedora in a back booth outscored everybody in the bakery fifty-to-zip. "Bullshit," Darren said and departed with the crowd. "What happened the night before last?" I asked the Quiz Night Champion once we were the only ones left in the bakery. "Don't talk to me," he said and peeled off his mustache. "You're trouble." "I know it," I said. "But at least I can grow a beard." The Quiz Night Champion removed his fedora; long black tresses fell past his shoulders. "The captain's wife," I said. "Heidi," she said. "I do have a name."

MUSICAL INTERLUDE

Heidi gave me a quick rundown on German philosophy as she drove us back to the ranch house. A guy by the name of Roy Orbison serenaded our post-coital cigarettes as I tried to get a mustache to stick to my forehead and Heidi explained that her biggest fear was to be known as a know-it-all. "That's strange," I said. She likewise explained that her husband had gotten confused by her costume and concluded she was meeting another man, when, in fact, she was that man. "Until tonight," I said. "Close enough," Heidi said. "But screw that guy. What sort of husband fakes his own death? He's just a frightened little boy lost in the woods." She began to tell me a story about the captain making a pass through a stand of secondary growth; Darren Wrath showed up in my dreams. "We share the same fate," he said and threw a profiterole at my face. "There's gold buried off the coast of a location I'm not at liberty to disclose. I have an inside source but I need an enthusiastic navigator." "I'm sort of in the middle of some things," I said. "No, you're not," Darren said and threw another profiterole. "What's so important? Think about it." I was awoken by a phone call. "It's happening again," Heidi said, handing over the receiver. "I'm not here." "Relax," I said, because I knew, without hearing his voice, that it wasn't the captain. "I'm coming with you," I said. "I've thought it over." "Well, it's about time," Darren said. "We liberate the captain's schooner at dawn. Pack sunscreen and a parasol." "Will a harpoon do?" I asked. There was a long pause; Heidi began to dress. "I suppose," Darren said. "But I'm nonplussed." "And I'm excited," I said. "But also scared." "Don't be scared," Darren said. "We both die on this trip. Resign yourself." Heidi was too busy with her buttons to be bothered with hanging up the phone; I didn't have time to talk her into staying. As I packed a duffel, I did my best to resign. Then I sat on the porch staring at the stars until the sun began to rise.

THE ENTHUSIASTIC NAVIGATOR

"Did I ever tell you about my days as a crack addict?" Darren asked while lowering the driver's side visor. "Not so as I can recollect," I said. "But I'm pretty sure it can happen to anybody." "And yet it didn't," Darren said. "Oh, right," I said, settling for an advertisement in place of an oldies station. "Would you like to talk about it?" "Not so much," Darren said. "There's very little I can remember, and we'll be scavenging at sea together a long, long time. Commence rationing." "Rationing," I said. "I hadn't thought of that. You must be an experienced sailor." Darren adjusted the rearview. "You do know how to sail, don't you?" I asked; Darren tapped the turn signal. "Maybe we should see if the Quiz Night Champion wants to come along." "Not on your life," Darren said. "If there's one thing I can't stand, it's a know-it-all." "A know-it-all?" I asked. "The biggest," Darren said and pulled into the parking lot of the wharf. "Take it back," I said. "No dice," Darren said. "I'm serious," I said. "Take it back or you're scavenging at sea all by your lonesome." "You'd never let that happen," Darren said. He cut the engine; I grabbed my harpoon from the trunk and was about to follow him toward the empty slip where the transparent schooner may or may not have been docked when I spotted Heidi standing outside the public restrooms at the edge of the parking lot. "Heidi!" I called, raising the harpoon above my head. "Heidi, over here!" The restrooms' door swung open, and a thin gentleman wearing a mustache and fedora stepped out. He placed an arm across Heidi's shoulders as the two of them stood there staring at some pink clouds above the point. Darren, meanwhile, stepped off the dock and splashed into the harbor.

WHAT'S THE DEAL WITH YOUR FRIEND?

"What's the deal with your friend?" an Eastern European waitress asked. "He's fine," I said as Darren shivered in a puddle. "A couple of profiteroles, please." The waitress shook her head but took her leave without further objection. "This place brings back some horrible memories," Darren said. "You're not alone there," I said and glanced at the booth where Heidi and I had shared a libation. "What do you think went wrong?" "I hear addiction is all about exposure," Darren said. "I blame my hometown." "I meant with the plan," I said as a couple of profiteroles were placed between us. "Plans are for pop tarts," Darren said. "What are these things?" "No idea," I said and picked one up. "So Heidi and the Quiz Night Champion… You knew about this?" "Everybody knew about this," Darren said. "Your memory's not so good, is it?" "Why would you say that?" I asked, and a big guy wearing a smock splattered with flour pulled up a chair. "Make yourself at home," Darren said. "Fuck off," the guy said and looked at me. "We have an opening."

ERICK VERRAN

Waiting for the Overnight to Toulouse

About the mountain
a hundred twirls of rose

testify Eastern sardanas.

Al meu jardí, a flower's
arranged to tell you.

In the middle of bus
terminals the green curls

through a coated bench.

And a jackal mewling in
blue-flowering herb.

Czech Fossil

Forty begonias, an axle
and its cartwheel—
the interstate's feral
courtyards' gnostic badge.

Circling a knoll in Prague
as I recall
the palisades in Florida,
cabled with mint and other
vine, are blowing.

Titian's Chariot

I have a soft spot for Titian's chariot, hauled by two
muscular leopards, who seem to recognize in silence

the yoke's mirror and an ordinary bond of paganism,
his mirthful faun bringing up a donkey's brown head.

QUENTIN MAHONEY

Pistis Sophia, Revisited

it's late afternoon
and i've been hangin around with some of the dirtier cocks on
   Smut St.

the sun boils low on the sky
like an old scabies scar picked raw by blistered tips
a crag-faced fellow hits a dry piano
for sounds that resonate
through a wine-stained aluminum tube in the crude hyperspace

Jinky bums a cigarette from a Bulldog and begins to speak:

"The Gnostics can't decide whether
God is still searching for us
or gave up entirely
but they agree
that the Demiurge is
bored with its creation

for all its power it could not predict,
when our nuclear duke sacrificed Sophia,
how vacuous to a King a Kingdom might be.
No, the Demiurge was not aware of dialectics
because it had to create a world for them to appear.

Not until his own subject wrote the Phenomenology
were the bounds of his ennui theoretically revealed

we could bring heaven to the world
the borders of our universe have relaxed with
his enthusiasm for rule.
porous now, the Light could drip in
but after a history beaten by sensation
would we even recognize it as the same blade
that ripped our own little tears in the fabric of Time?

look how the low sun bleeds orange
through pores in the sulfurous sky

the chromatic range of this world is dulling with
the erotic excitement our monarch once had for power
yes, he wants us to cast off his yoke
and lie in fields of our own
that is what Sophia told us would happen
that all narratives end in
an ecstatic moment of unshackling
but he did his job too well when he killed her
Sophia

but now, as in Stockholm, we are
home in our homesickness
satisfied where we are forlorn
an Odysseus who chose to eat the lotus
not because it was sweet, but because it was there."

The ash of Jinky's cigarette is unbroken
a perfect carbon pillar

i cough and something comes up
mechanically i swallow it back down

the crag-faced fellow with the dry piano
     has been singing along the whole time:

        "improper machines we are
        rat poison, it's a bitch doc,
        but man what a high!"

MICHAEL KIMBALL

Two People Can Go Amazing

I pull the sky blanket up over her apple waist in the back and place a fat pillow against the broken wall behind her. How long does it take to get some sleep if I wake up every time I think and it breaks? The bright air hurts my ocean eyes, but I keep them open until I see her hip flexion between the dry smother and the beautiful light. I hand-hug the sides of her lucky face, however, looking at me, I realize something went down wrong for her to sleep.

I want to say something before it's too late: critical lying is okay now. Two brothers, they have the forgotten names of the surviving family, and I like to say I'm well treated in the rebuilt concrete. The rendered cases against the pre-history don't know the name of my previous allegiance anymore. I have never smoothed out a real person, but I want the name of the drama killer. Do dead people love you or doesn't that consolidated emotion exist anymore? She contacts touch and disseminates as far away as possible in the information format.

We're not auxiliary people trapped here and I cannot be the other person between us. Can you say anything when you open your salad mouth or are your thoughts jumping around? I could not get all the florid words to form a complete set. I felt something in my twisted stomach when her pinecone head rolled sideways. Everything stopped going to the upper incline and I don't know where to report for the task table. Can you concentrate after the deluxe freeze occurs or will it go to spare overtime? My inside blood begins to penetrate the necessary sleep to all parts of my opening body. I turn the inside power off and begin to tremble.

I hide under an anonymous table to cover myself, so I don't feel raw flow or too cold. All the included ideas are bounded gaps beyond the harbor. I cracked and she dwindled, but otherwise I'm sure we are a good addition, and I don't want to end our talking relationship. I throw foreign things against the broken wall, but I'm made of fractured glass, and we're trying to stop the uncharted onslaught. She fears bigger eyes for their expression recognition and she doesn't act like strange refreshment. She remains beautifully damaged and I hope that prolonging her means she can stay with me as a garnished reminder.

Also, she wants to be the opposite case, but I don't think it's frosty or statuesque. She works with radical games that never meet in the high fields and her sleeping retention returns her to a nameless home almost every night. Did you stop at the residual house before she wakes up? Should the penultimate action of her foundling company seem bewitching? What relief she finds with the lock and key doubles as a general feeling before she gives me the full lean.

After the submission of the missing report, I don't believe buttonhole appeals either. It must be something different between us, but sometimes I have this terrible thing where I fool my teeth. Is this up and down enough or do I have the wild knife in the wrong direction? The erroneous shape of my fried face goes intricate and lace. The perfect shape for your baroque face crosses the great divide of space between the eyes and mouth. The secret zipper man and I start an inexact laugh, but then we overnight through the polarized forestation. I help others wire the decision circle, but we require better refreshment than those with the new pre-history. It has to be false to maintain this desolate space. The disoriented treatment of mercury waste by a candy doctor will not save her fake nose.

Did you leave a barbaric home with the trapped colors and check the worksheet boxes? Please do not crack open the wig-head and place it on the tabletop or the table legs will promenade. Open up the head shape of the worst void and then guess anybody who it could be. This is especially bad eyesight in the future, but she's my clear and final choice. Did you know that two people can go amazing for so long? We already know it took more end time, but I did not understand this until the outlandish report of the rotating fog began to lead us. I hate to change my family name, but we didn't fight last night. She did not seduce me with her evolution, but she touched me frontally around alternative people. Are you past remote happiness or do you pretend to have exiled satisfaction?

I'm buzzy tired, so I don't want to feel alone. I throw my unnerved arms around her estranged world, but she begins to lament, and I can feel the liquid sharpness of her derived tears on my tilted neck. Do you need to tell me about the head weakness? I didn't expect her to be so externally constitutional, but I had forgotten how to feel good. This fake embarrassment, it's nothing special, so maybe she can stay with me here even if it means the end of our horizon days.

ESTER NAOMI PERQUIN

TRANSLATED BY DAVID COLMER

So to Speak

Anyway now you're here, I wrote you letters and never
mailed them, learned your number by heart
and mumbled it aimlessly to myself,
gradually taking your existence
personally.

I rented a house on the shore and had your name
engraved alongside mine on a brass plate.
Such well-matched initials, the man said.
An auspicious sign.

No need for you to pay that any mind of course.
It's not as if I'm going to turn up naked
late one night to put on a show,
don't think that.

But with things between us going so well
I thought it would be nice if you
were in on it too.
That's why.

APRIL BERNARD

Found Sonnet: Samuel Johnson

—from Rambler, *No. 5*

When a man cannot bear his own company
there is something wrong. He must fly
from himself, either because he feels a tediousness
in life from the equipoise of an empty mind,
which, having no tendency
to one motion more than another
but as it is impelled by some external power,
must always have recourse to foreign objects;
or he must be afraid of the intrusion of unpleasing ideas,
and, perhaps, is struggling to escape
from the remembrance of a loss, the fear of a calamity,
or some other thought of greater horror.

A French author has advanced this seeming paradox,
that *very few men know how to take a walk.*

Werner Herzog in the Amazon

HIS WORDS TO LES BLANK
IN THE DOCUMENTARY *BURDEN OF DREAMS*

We are challenging nature itself
and it hits back, it hits back, we have to accept
that it's much stronger than we are:
Fornication and asphyxiation
and choking and fighting for survival and growing and
just rotting away. The trees are in misery
and the birds are in misery. I don't think
they sing, they just screech in pain.

It's a land that God, if he exists, has created
in anger. Take a close look
at what's around us: overwhelming and collective murder.
And we, in comparison to the articulate vileness
of all this jungle,
we only sound like a badly pronounced
and half-finished sentence
out of a stupid suburban novel.

We have to become humble
in front of this overwhelming misery and
overwhelming fornication,
overwhelming growth and overwhelming
lack of order. Here
even the stars in the sky
look like a mess.

I say this all
full of admiration for the jungle.
It is not that I hate it—
I love it, but I love it
against my better judgment.

Samaria

Over the deep gorge a bird
circles. Called
"the attorney buzzard,"
he deliberatively draws
a bridge on the air
from one edge of the rim to the sky.
(We cannot walk on air.)
Sudden I smell mimosa,
incongruous as
the drag of your feet, departing
this world
against your will,
against the sun itself.

When I Was Thirteen, I Saw Uncle Vanya

A handful of yellow roses
                              trailing on the stage;
a woman sitting idle on a swing;
charts of "the district"
                        spread over the floor
while a man and woman
who should not,
               should,
                     should not
kiss   leaned over them;
confusion and weeping;
the harness bells shimmering
                        as the doctor left;
someone saying what he must not say
                          and then
everyone agreeing it had never been said;
the strange ways music and knocking
came and went—

I kissed the doctor,
I fired the wild shots,
I strummed the guitar,
I poured the tea and
                    dropped the roses
and drank too much and said

"Excuse me, I am without a necktie."
I said, "Live, for once in your life!"

Above me, what I had always called   "sky"
revealed itself a sham:
I took my shiny new knife   and slashed
through the blue paper,

                              to see instead: The real sky,

the high wind bunching and boiling the clouds, and past them,

the unfathomable, planets orange, blue-and-white,
    magnificent—

Because when I was thirteen, I saw *Uncle Vanya*.

Trying to Like Spenser

Refusal of wit in favor, here, of a knight

in armour so untarnished it glares white—
and on a white horse whose neck curves back
and back, only to bow in swoop, low as if to graze
the greensward, swings low his noble head
as the queen, not faerie-gauzed today but also metalled
ice-white, arrives astride her own white horse.

So hard to take, these apparitions of magnificence

meeting one another in a dark green wood.
They make their own clearing, as we clutch
at *allegory* and then lose it again, it slips away
as even the trees curtsey, abashed by unfamiliar light,
and willow leaves, elves' eyes, shut to silver
and dip low in their own imperceptible breeze.

Just to confuse you, maze on over

and far enough off: in a stubble field six falcons post
in circle aloft, as a foreign knight, black-plumed
and armoured copper red, lies pooled in the crimson
of life poured out his throat. Disdain *symbol*.
A quest, a duel, a murderous errand gone awry?
Mourn him as the sun signals its noon.

Comes an intrusive personal thought:

this noon casts a light I sudden remember
from home movies in Super 8, at the beach,
when the camera's eye slid from perfect blue horizon,
from tomato red-and-yellow stripes of bathing suits,
the checked blanket, the false and silent merry gawping,
up, to the sun itself, burnt white, burnt out.

Now a mossy problem 'mid linnets' clamour, that

in the cool green wood we cannot hear one word
the knight and his queen speak. We guess, since his cross
of red blazes, they plot holy-wise. Unless—fearful thought—
she is no queen but disguised. The horses nicker parley,
some long-standing joke. How I would rather
confer with beasts, breathe in their sour apple air.

Muttering a seemly oath, *by Mary's nose*, I see

that plot full-veiled is Romance unmasked. Let us
tally measures of heavy loveliness, rods' lengths
tapestries of Persia green and Paris blue tugged
from white flanks, tossed to the grass. He and she,
uncarapaced to whitest linen, curl in dalliance
upon silk-broidered peacocks and swans aswim.

It is in the nature of this ordeal, my own crusade

to tame my infidel taste, to continue knowing
that the story of virtue cannot proceed without
the flaring-forth of those gaudy charms and rhymes
that I am since childhood too proud to wear. I choose
dissection and deflection; deeper still lies something
about trust and the wondering largely thereon.

Yet while thus color-stunned, we forgot to ask

where now?—for knight and queen are gone. What
task will queen—glorious one, brittle martial one,
fiend of duplicity, or glitter-cluttered she-bird,
I cannot sort the ladies out and never could—
or knight of tiresome goodness next undertake
with lance or mirror, gilt-hilt dagger or carven cup?

As slight pain swivets my skull, I frantic turn pages

to peasants dancing, delving, and complaining
about the month of March. Join me now: Slap through
those sweetmeat sonnets that stick to your molars,
uxorious bragalamia; and misty notes in which
the poet praises himself. Yet flee though we try, stupored
we are reeled back in to that epic that has no end.

We escape our *Faerie* never; mayhap the last leaves

were burnt up in a fire; the story only pauses. Here
they come again, or else their doubles: knight scaling a cliff
to scold Rue, queen sneering at the moon in stanzas
right casually metered. Elsewhere a maiden (fair)
in kirtle (green) plucks and sings. I hear the lute now,
its ravishing tune I can almost bring myself to hum:

claw-shape the chord: again *strum*, and ever and anon.

E.O. NESSUNA

Thirteen Cakes for Ignazio

It was to nobody's surprise that Vincenzo Abandonato became a father by unusual means. He told me about it in Buenos Aires, during our first dinner together. I was on my honeymoon.

This dinner was arranged by a mutual friend, Mari, who had of course been sleeping with Cenzo at the time, though we didn't know it until later, not that it was really any of our business. She was the type to do perilous non-profit work in border towns and hinterlands, and she was perhaps the most delicate and whitest-looking person I'd ever known. Her skin was translucent, bordering on transparent, rice-paper-esque, her yellow hair starchy as summer bleached hay. She had sharp features, a stiletto nose, a tiny and lithe, tight little boyish physique. She was a righteous, strong, and healthy do-gooder, an uncomplicated yoga fanatic, a raw foodie—that kind of person. She made an audio documentary on the conflict in Chiapas, and ran an organization that brought film screenings and books to refugee camps in sub-Saharan Africa. She was seemingly forever on the mend from one kind of intestinal parasite or another, carried Cipro and iodine in her makeup case.

Living in Buenos Aires between stints in the rural outback, Mari had become friends with a local chef named Diego, who ran a so-called secret kitchen out of his large, empty colonial apartment. It was on the creative outskirts of a dilapidated neighborhood, which felt shut tight, the unseen denizens behind steel grates, barred windows, and ancient, locked front doors.

At the dinner were Mari, Cenzo, myself, and my brand-new husband, Eric, as well as our friend Yams, and his friend Dimitri. There were, I think, a couple of other people down the other end of the table but I can't be sure. They could have been strangers, thinking about it now. It was dark, there was a lot of wine, a little bit of hash. I'm not positive. And I can't remember now how I even knew Yams, but he'd been a friend forever. Yams was from Connecticut and had found a job just out of college as F-C's personal driver. A decade later he had worked his way up to a full-fledged producer. The current production crew was stationed in Argentina for six months while F-C shot a feature and simultaneously converted a residential palazzo into a micro-hotel in a dicey, emerging district. Dimitri was the cinematographer on the film. He was a funny little Romanian guy with thick glasses, and after I often wondered what lightning strike of good fortune got this Roman from nowhere linked up with a film legend like F-C. He must have been good.

Diego and his wife, I never caught her name, were of the superlatively hip Argentine artist class; she with strange Euro-style half-shaved haircut and multiple piercings, he with a soft baby face and tattoo sleeves, a regard for the earth and for doing things the old-fashioned way. The meal was entirely local, of course, in season, of course, and prepared without menu. We were served everything from salad to dessert, with various boozes in between, and told what we were eating only a few moments after we had forked it into our mouths. It was delicious, or at least it was pretty good, and all of us got drunk and loud and hot in the face in the dark and sparse dining room, sitting on benches, voices and glasses clinking off the stucco walls. Afterward, we sat in the back patio listening to the soft sounds of traffic in the distance and talking about the future while Diego and his wife scurried the dishes into the sink. We smoked and drank more. I smoked way too much, compulsively, because Eric had allowed me a cease-fire from the torture of my painful, never-ending Quit while on my honeymoon. In those days my addiction roared loudly, constantly, over my own thoughts. This is where Cenzo and I became fast friends, I told him about my own films and my writing and aspirations, determinations, and about my upbringing; I was young-ish and forward-looking and he, looking back, and, perhaps, looking around, told me about his son.

THE STORY RAN SOMETHING LIKE THIS: ABOUT fourteen years ago, Cenzo was out drinking with some friends one night, first at a long dinner then a long night of dancing and wandering drunkenly, stupidly, around Rome. They had gotten brain-splittingly wasted on wine and who knows what else, and at dinner a lengthy discussion ran on and on about the state of gay rights in Italy. Two of the women in the group were dating each other—very, very seriously dating each other. They believed they were soul mates. And Italy being what it is and has always been, Catholic and bizarrely backwards in matters of social justice, especially where sex and femininity are involved, the couple couldn't get married or even attain any kind of stable domestic partner status. As they so desperately wished. And they felt they really also ought not to have children, given the insurmountable prejudice, the custodial uncertainty afforded by Italian law. And this even though they were ready, they wanted a child, were desperate for a child, a little person to love and raise and care for and lavish all the emotional extravagances on in the typical Italian way. They wanted to become a family. We've heard this kind of thing before.

A debate followed that covered both the practical truths of quotidian life in Italy and the harshness of material realism which turned into chest-thumping and table-pounding and unchecked howling defenses of true love and denouncements of the injustices of post-post-modernity and curses of biology and questions of destiny. All got drunker and drunker, louder and louder, gesticulating, emotional. These were, after all, Italians, and they were discussing matters of the heart, and impossible love, and inequality before an unjust law. And so things got emphatic, tears were shed, proclamations were made. And Cenzo, a man who wrote his graduate thesis on the topic of disobedience at age twenty-three, had plenty to say. At one point he stood up and raised a glass to the two obstructed lovers and made a vow to donate his sperm to them *the very next day* so that they could live their dream, they could create life, make a baby and start a family. Because what is Italy if not a country of Love and Dreams and *Famiglia*? Fuck the mafia, fuck Berlusconi and his corrupt government, fuck the Catholic church. *Omnia vincit amor. L'amore conquista tutti*. Love conquers all.

All intoned: "*Saluti*" and drained their glasses before Cenzo had to sit down on his fat ass, then be taken home in a taxi, his shoes removed by two friends, his robust body rolled onto his couch and laid on his side for safety, a trash bin positioned just so, his lights turned off and his door shut quietly behind.

He awoke the next day to the ringing of his mobile phone at 1 PM, throwing it across the room. At 2 PM he rolled over and vomited into the trash bin left thoughtfully by his side. At 3 PM he gathered the strength to sit up and wobble to the bathroom, vomit again, then root around his fridge for some leftover gnocchi con pesto, a hard boiled egg, a half glass of Peroni, and some wafer cookies. By 5 PM he was feeling human again, which was a relief, and convenient, too, as just at that moment his buzzer began to buzz, incessantly. He thought at first it must be the gypsy woman who frequently tried to sneak into his building by pressing every buzzer at the front door and asking for "Gianni" or "Maria." But when the buzzing persisted, and persisted and persisted, and took on an almost comical, friendly sort of tone, little ditties and rhythms, "Shave and a haircut… BUZZ BUZzzzzzzz," sounding over and over, Cenzo dragged himself from the table and hollered into the intercom.

"What," he said.

"It's us!" said one of the women of forbidden love from the night before.

"Who?"

"Us! Anna and Domi," said Anna. Or Domi. "We have to leave *now*. The clinic closes at seven!"

This gave Cenzo pause. Clinic? He knew Anna and Domi, of course. They weren't his best friends by any stretch, but he had known them around his scene for a number of years. He vaguely remembered they had been at the dinner. But the clinic? He tried to reach back into the fog of the night before, but he couldn't place the context. There was something nagging, however, something hazily familiar, something that pricked him that was disturbing. Or not disturbing but...worrying. Or disturbing, yes, it was entirely disturbing.

Cenzo pressed the talkback button on the intercom and paused for a moment before saying: "The clinic?"

"*Si, si. La clinica di sperma*," said Domi or Anna, adding a "*cazzo*" for good measure. Cenzo released the talkback and banged his head against the wall. Then it came back to him all in a flush. The toasts, the promises, the proclamations. What an ass he was. And how did he get home? Never mind. He was going to donate his sperm, so what. He knew he would. It was a foregone conclusion. It was the kind of thing he would have to do, because he was Cenzo. He was who he was and he knew he would do it. He couldn't resist the draw of the disobedience, the draw of the experience, of the story, the narrative. Without so much as a thought to the future, to the meaning of depositing his bodily fluid into a little capsule and handing it off and leaving it behind. Without so much as a thought to the child who would, could, might be born of this hasty decision. Weren't children always born of hasty decisions? Or mostly? Even under natural conditions?

He stopped himself from using the word "natural" in his brain, as a feminist and a proponent of disruption and progress he learned to avoid words such as "natural" and "normal." Because it implied a judgment, a betterness, to the traditional ways, to the more common ways. He and other liberal-minded people around the world groped for and found other ways of expressing it that were less binary, more inclusive. Because jacking off in a third floor clinic down the hall from an internet marketing startup and a small language school attended mostly by Arabs and Africans, then catching the sperm in a small receptacle and allowing it to be refrigerated and then injected via turkey baster or whatever into the vagina of a lesbian he was acquainted with but not really friends with wasn't exactly *unnatural*. Nature includes practically everything we humans do, doesn't it? We are animals, we are part of nature, our behaviors are all natural. It was simply unusual. It was simply new. It was disobedient, and it really was a vision Cenzo saw before it even happened. His life up to this point had been a wandering series of partial-attempts, half-failures, missed connections. And so it felt as though he had no choice, as though the situation had chosen him instead.

"Come on up," said Cenzo and buzzed the women into the building. He put up some water for coffee and tried to straighten the kitchen, caught sight of his unshaven face in the mirror and grinned. He was going to become a father after all, handsome dog that he was, even after all those years of chasing women and never settling down, never committing. Here he was jumping into a threesome, a complicated, bizarre, uncharted relationship. He did as he pleased and maybe, in the end, he would still win at life. There it was: another vindication, though he caught himself, tried to check himself from viewing things in a competitive light. The important point was that he would still, of course, be free. They would work out the details later. Later. There was always time for that kind of thing.

He opened the door and Anna and Domi pressed into his place.

"You're not backing out are you?" asked Domi.

"Of course not," said Cenzo. He was feeling rather magnanimous and grand.

"You were fucking wasted last night, Cenz," said Anna. "We were afraid you might've forgotten."

"Please," said Cenzo, placing a hand over his heart. "I am a man of my word." He told them to make themselves at home while he jumped in the shower.

As the water dribbled over his head Cenzo's mind was a blank. In the living room, Anna and Domi looked around his apartment with curiosity. So this was the man they were choosing. Anna was uncertain because, well, look at the place. It was a mess. Domi waved her off.

"Baby, don't be so picky," she said. "He's great." Domi paused, then continued. "He's good. He's good."

Cenzo's dirty underwear sat inert on the couch, stained green, with pesto probably. Anna picked it up with the assistance of a pencil. "Really?"

Domi put her arms around Anna and said, "We're going to be a family. So he's a manly man. A strong, Italian man with good sturdy sperm, probably—"

Anna laughed.

"At least he's not a 'donor,' you know," said Domi. They had discussed the issues they'd read about that were happening in places where this kind of thing was more lax, like in America, where men became official donors, took the role on almost as a second job, or a strange, perverted hobby, giving sperm again and again and again, fathering dozens and dozens of children, who then would meet out in the world and, possibly, date, fuck, procreate, whatever, while not knowing they were, in fact, half-siblings. Americans as usual jumped into it too fast without thinking about the ramifications, and now they were pulling back, making registries and the like. Now the inter-generational, multi-hued American children of these professional donors would have big dinners together once a year, without the donor-father because to hell with him anyway. They would fly across the continent, even, to learn about and acquaint themselves with their brothers and sisters, virtual strangers connected by a batch of a sample left by a potentially dubious man with potentially dubious motives.

At that moment the sound of Cenzo hawking and spitting in the shower, and farting, emanated into the living room. Anna raised an eyebrow, and both women laughed. They were lucky, they were skirting the process. No adoption papers, no lying, or obfuscating the truth, no searching through redacted donor profiles and wondering who and what-if. This was a real man in the flesh whom they knew, whom they even loved on some level, whom they respected and who believed in what they were doing, and who was doing it just once, just for them.

They had decided that Anna would carry the baby as she was the more maternal one, the more feminine one, the one who would glow from her skin and shine from her hair and read the magazines. She was almost forty, however, and for this reason, and also to give Domi equal connection with the child, they would use Domi's egg. Domi was just thirty and the picture of perfect, ruddy, androgynous health. They had already harvested a dozen from her ovaries and had them cooling in a fridge in a facility near the Vatican. This made Anna and Domi laugh. The irony of it. If the Pope only knew, Domi would say, making the sign of the cross, kissing her fingers and looking to the sky, mouthing some kind of supplication. Anna wasn't sure whether Domi was kidding or not, because although she was a stone-cold, committed lesbian, at base level she was religious, came from a traditional Sicilian family, and revered the Madonna. No matter how many university classes she took, no matter how much she opened herself sexually to Anna, no matter how confident she grew in her identity as a modern person, she couldn't shake the reverence to the Madonna. Blessed Mary, Mother of God.

Back in her old town, a tiny village about an hour outside the central Sicilian city of Caltanisetta, with its two main cathedrals and endless traffic jams down winding medieval streets, Domi would go to church. To the simple and honest church closest to her family's apartment, where the statue of the Madonna was excruciatingly brutal and grotesque, her heart pierced with not one, not two, but twelve daggers, and blood seeping from her heart, bloody tears from her eyes.

"Isn't she beautiful?" said Domi, kneeling before her Madonna, the Madonna she had known as a child, her first Madonna, her comfort-Madonna.

At this, Anna, who was raised in Milan by atheists, her father a successful banker, her mother a revered professor of psychology, chuckled. She thought Domi was joking. But then she noticed the whiteness spreading from Domi's knuckles, her hands clasped tightly and pressed to her lips, her head bent over, her knee on the hard stone floor, her eyes shut tight. Anna cut her laughter with a cough.

"She is, quite beautiful," Anna said. It seemed to Anna that Domi had been moved to tears, fighting them, apologizing for her existence to the Madonna, seeking forgiveness, ever seeking forgiveness for her difference from the norm. Anna's throat closed at the tragedy of the situation and she wanted to embrace her lover, but knew that Domi would not want it; it would not have been appropriate in this church, not ever, not even when empty.

AFTER CENZO SHOWERED AND DRESSED AND GRABBED a few more bites of cold pasta direct from the fridge with his thick fingers, the trio went downstairs to the cafe to have a quick espresso. Although they were in a rush Cenzo felt he needed it and being Italians in a situation such as this, regardless of time constraints, there was no refusing. Cenzo must have what he wants. Anna and Domi both understood and didn't need to communicate this between them. After Cenzo shot the espresso in one gulp to the back of his throat along with a swallow of anise liquor, and left a couple of euro coins on the immaculate copper bar, Domi drove them to the clinic in her black Cinquecento with red trim, Anna wedged in the rear, Cenzo jammed in the front like a teddy bear squished into a tin box by a small child.

All the way there they spoke of anything but the impending act. Berlusconi, always a favorite. A recently translated novel by Bolaño and the idiotic conversion of a main artery of Rome to a one-way street. Domi cursed as she arched back, reversing the car down the street and around a corner.

Domi flogged the Cinquecento, racing through the cobblestone piazze of this everlasting, pulsing, decomposing capital city of seven hills. Anna could feel Domi's excitement manifested through her impulsive driving. And the deep baritones of Cenzo's voice, and the knowledge, unspoken, that this man in the car would get himself hard and climax for them within the hour lent a surprising sexuality to the journey for Anna. She had been with one man during university and it was rough and quick but the memory of it had stayed with her. She didn't find it hotly erotic, as the image of a woman's body, but she thought of it from time to time. Now she felt a rush of blood to her most tender spots. She hung on to the handles on the roof of the car as Domi swung around a curve, flipping off another driver by flicking four fingers from under her chin.

"*Vaffanculo pezzo di merda*," Domi said, flat, almost matter-of-factly.

THE WOMEN REMAINED IN THE WAITING ROOM as Cenzo performed his duty, quickly and without drama. He was surprised by how easy it was, and how unaffected he was by the clinical atmosphere. He was certain that the highly ethical and benevolent motive behind his donation was the reason it came so readily. He could imagine the shame and filth that would come with masturbating in this clinic for money, or for a perverse thrill. No. He was doing it to help some nice girls, some beautiful women who were in love, in impossible love with each other, to conceive and have a child in this fucked-up world. It was a beautiful thing he was doing, and thus he came quickly and guiltlessly. As soon as it was over he invited the girls to dinner. They agreed, and they all went to an osteria down the street.

Domi and Anna were in the highest of spirits, kissing and caressing in public, even though it was nowhere near accepted behavior, even in Rome, a so-called metropolitan kind of town, and even though this was an upscale place with one long communal table where other diners could not hide their salacious interest in this intense trinity's conversation. Cenzo treated himself to a full four-course meal: first an antipasto of lightly fried artichokes, then a pasta course of spaghetti alle vongole, then a meat course of grilled lamb chops in rosemary, olive oil, and sea salt, and finally a dessert of tiramisu and a small glass of sweet wine. All told, the three polished off two and a half bottles of wine and smoked a pack of cigarettes, filling the ashtray to overflowing twice. Cenzo did most of the indulging, and everyone was happy. When the bill came, Cenzo insisted on paying, even though Domi and Anna demanded he let them take him out, after what he had just done for them. But he was feeling far too magnanimous to let them pay. He was a man, and he really felt like one tonight, and he was happy.

THIS IS THE PART OF THE STORY where Cenzo cleared his throat and asked Diego to bring another beer out to the backyard. His voice grew somber, and I lit cigarette after cigarette, entranced by his story. Eric interrupted quietly to ask if I wanted something more to eat, but I declined, and he went back to chatting with Mari, reminiscing about our college days which had been, at that moment, not that far in the past.

After the brief evening at the clinic and the dinner at the osteria, Cenzo had to fly to Mallorca to produce a commercial for Alitalia, and then stayed on to produce a commercial for an international sportswear retailer, then stayed on yet another three weeks to produce a spot for a German cheese company. When he returned to Rome, he fell quickly in love with a woman named Rivi, an Israeli who grew up on a commune outside Tel Aviv and who had moved to Rome to finish her novel. Their love affair was passionate, "we fucked constantly," said Cenzo, with his usual tact, but fizzled quickly. Cenzo, though sneaking toward middle age, had never had a relationship last longer than three months. And, heartbroken, he left Rome for Amsterdam where he lived for eight months studying yoga and occasionally working on the odd television documentary. Despite the constantly fluctuating economy, for males of a certain class it didn't take much to live as a bachelor in the EU, where fine things were everywhere and wine and cheese were considered essentials and home was always just a train ride away. It was here that Cenzo cemented his knowledge of English.

Years went by before Cenzo realized he had neither seen nor heard from Anna and Domi since that fateful night. He tried to find them online, and made a few half-hearted phone calls, but couldn't locate them. He didn't expend too much energy looking, but still, it was odd that he had never realized how tangential their relationship had been. They were not part of his central group of friends, and not on the perimeter of the group, not even on the outskirts. He couldn't find anyone who could tell him anything about what had happened to the women. They had vanished like a puff of dandelion fuzz from his past.

Cenzo spent one long, lonely morning thinking about it, this time wandering the pleasant streets of his boyhood neighborhood in Milan. He came to the comfortable conclusion that they probably never had the baby, because otherwise he'd have known about it. They probably had had trouble conceiving, their plan was so absurd and unnecessarily complicated, anyway, he thought. Or they could have broken up before they were able to make the baby. Yes, that was the most likely explanation. If it looks like a duck and walks like a duck, Occam's razor and all that. The hypothesis with the fewest assumptions should be selected. They were women, and everyone would agree that women are volatile lovers and impulsive, emotional partners, and that when you get two of them together into one relationship, the outcome is most likely a rash of heated, passionate, knock-down, drag-out fights that last long into the late hours, the kind where you forget at four in the morning the original nugget of the fight but where you keep going, because you must, because your dignity is on the line and you feel you must be respected. Those things usually lead to pained, tearful, and irreparable breakups, and that's probably what happened to Anna and Domi. They seemed sort of mismatched, too, thought Cenzo. Domi was so boyish and Anna was so absolutely ravishing and feminine, it was hard to rationalize her gayness and her attraction to Domi. Oh well, thought Cenzo, and carried on with his life.

"SO..." SAID CENZO AS HE LEANED CLOSE to me, lit a cigarette for himself off the burning end of mine, "fourteen years later..."

"*No,*" I said.

"Yes," said Cenzo. He was savoring my attention.

"No," I said.

"Yes. Yes!" he said, ever more emphatic, and continued.

By now Eric, Mari, Yams, and Dimitri had joined us in a little circle to hear the rest of the story. Eric put a sweater around my shoulders against the darkening night.

About a year ago, Cenzo said, he had gotten a tentative and nervous call from Anna, who, in a guarded voice, asked him if he would like to meet his son. She was reluctant actually to divulge anything about the situation, including their whereabouts. Cenzo was stunned and ecstatic to hear that he had a son in the world. He had never settled down, and went on and on with his short-term flings with women from around the world, never hanging onto any one because of his chronic wandering eye. But that did not mean he wouldn't like to have a son. What kind of man would deny the existence of that powerful urge to father a son in this world? And guess what? The boy was already thirteen.

Cenzo clapped his hands with glee and invoked Jesus, Mary, and Joseph with sufficient irony. All the hard work was done. He had no dirty diapers to change, no table manners to teach. Now the boy was a ripe adolescent on the brink of manhood, poised to receive all the fatherly guidance he had been missing for his past thirteen years. Cenzo was overjoyed, truly overjoyed.

He met the boy, whose name was Ignazio after Domi's father, and who carried a powerful physical resemblance to Cenzo. He exuded a wonderful, sweet temperament. Sure, he needed masculine guidance, and Cenzo was there, happy to give it in measured doses. Cenzo had moved to Buenos Aires and was only back in Italy for holidays. He couldn't stand what he felt was withering criticism from his father, Salvatore, and his more traditionally successful older brother, Salvatore, Jr. He felt stifled and unwell when in Milan, and tried to spend as little time in Italy as possible. Now Cenzo made exceptions to visit Ignazio, who lived in Rome with his mothers.

"I bought him a PlayStation," said Cenzo. I was surprised by the decadent, lowbrow, typically American impulse, but then again, children are children, the world over.

"He loves his PlayStation," said Cenzo.

I asked Cenzo if his mother had met Ignazio.

"Of course!" he said. She was overcome with emotion by the idea that an unknown grandson had been out in the world, just a few hundred kilometers away, ungrandmothered and unloved all this time. For their initial meeting she baked him thirteen cakes to make up for all the birthdays she had missed.

"It is the Italian Way," said Cenzo, grinning with unguarded pride in his mother's excessive love; her devotion to him reflected in her outsized affection for her newly acquired grandchild. Cenzo showed us a picture of Ignazio on his phone, and there he was, fat with curly black hair and a devious smile, Cenzo's devious smile, gazing out of the phone's background. We all marveled at the likeness, as we knew we should.

I asked Cenzo about his relationship to the mothers.

"It is very strained," he said, frowning. "There is competition."

According to Cenzo, the Italian law that prevented Anna and Domi from getting married, and refused them protection as a couple in the first place, also granted Cenzo, if he chose to exercise it, the right to full paternity and full custody of the child.

"Ignazio very much wants to be with me as much as he can, of course, it's only natural for a boy. Anna and Domi are afraid I will take him away from them at any moment," he said in his precise, learned English. "Although I have assured them over and over I have no interest, they are afraid Ignazio will provoke it. They have no rights. I have all the power. But I have my life here in Buenos Aires. So I stay away."

Of course I couldn't help but wonder if this was the true reason behind his exile from Italy. I understood at that moment that Cenzo had never felt the burning sensation of true loneliness until the moment he learned he had Ignazio. He sat thinking about the situation and sighed.

"It's very sad," he said, looking at the ground and taking a drag on his cigarette, his thoughts suddenly far off. "It is the Italian Way."

AND IN THAT PLACE, AMONG STRANGERS, I knew Cenzo had to be in some way related to me, a distant cousin, or even a brother, reunited after a wayward cycle of lifetimes. There was something entirely distasteful about him: dark, shameful, self-obsessed, undisciplined, debauched, and yet, in many ways, profoundly familiar, similar to me. It was strange. I lit another cigarette and thanked God for it and wondered if I would ever quit, ever give myself up to imperfection and forgo struggling for good.

And more, since our meeting was inadvertent, and occurred on neither of our home continents, our regular lives so distant, I thought for sure that it would turn out to be one of those quirks of time, two twists of moonlight crossing at a precise point, never to cross again, and that all these people from this earthy communal table would disperse and I would never see Cenzo again, but of course, I was wrong.

ELLIOT REED

Slice Hypotenuse

In Bob's early drawings you see both of us. They're pastels, done on the backs of huge sheets of drafting paper he found in a dumpster behind the architecture school. Then, as now, Bob applies the colors in layers heavy enough to make the paper curl. You know it's meant to be Bob, in the early pictures, because of the eye makeup and the thin little mustache. You know it's me because of the curly blonde hair, the protruding ears, and the color of my skin, which Bob makes by rubbing a finger in the pastel on the page, then adding more color and mixing it again until it's perfect. In Bob's first drawing of us, we're floating ten feet above an endless desert plain. It's night (the night sky is coal), but you can see mountains in the distance, pale brown in the moonlight, slopes rising from the chalky black. Between us, standing stiffly upright in a red suit, is a man with the head of a llama. The llama-man stares straight out at you with his hands cupped, outstretched, beneath our floating feet, like he's selling us: he's saying, what are they worth to you?

Lately, Bob's been drawing on the cardboard boxes I bring home from work. In one drawing, I'm shirtless, in a pine forest, using an eight-foot crowbar to sabotage a logging railroad. I've got the rail up with the metal bar, and I'm looking at a plume of steam coming over the tips of nearby trees. You can't really tell what's going through my head; I'm either a seasoned terrorist, or I'm too terrified to think. All Bob's drawings are two-dimensional. The ones where I'm the only person are just more two-dimensional than the others. In another, I'm floating over a series of impossible rapids in a birch-bark canoe. The water's not even touching my boat. Again, my face reveals nothing. I tell

Bob his best works are the ones without me, the ones he stopped making right after we moved in together: the self-portrait, for example, that I saw the night I met him. It's as good as a van Gogh, and even more colorful. Still, I don't know what I'd do if Bob stopped drawing me.

I MET BOB A YEAR AGO. I was heading to a night class when I found him in an alcove. He was playing the accordion, dressed like a 1920s flapper girl, and two dimes were in the bottom of an overturned hat in front of him. That self-portrait was on the ground, held down by a rock on each corner.

He was beautiful and talented, and we were both still so young, so I decided to put off school for a while. I took a full-time job at GoBig Foods and found us an apartment—a place where Bob could work all day on his art. He stayed at home, I went to work. At work I'd stock shelves and pour food from huge bags into big blue barrels—bulk bins the customers dug from with little plastic shovels.

I RODE MY BIKE TO MY NEW job. It was June, and I was a week into training. The weather outside was abnormally hot, and the ride to work was all uphill. I changed in the bathroom at work, using wet wipes to scrub my pits beside a toilet that auto-flushed over and over unless I stood pressed against the bathroom wall. I got the routine down to a minute flat. If I took longer than a minute and a half, someone would knock on the door. Usually it was one of the floor managers, and usually they would act suspicious when I came out. They assigned me aisles and a stained apron, a locker in the break room, and a box cutter.

On the ride home I kept my front tire on the asphalt veins painted over old cracks in the sidewalk. The tire was low, and if I hit any potholes the beer I was carrying for Bob would fizz when he opened it. Eventually I got to the bike trail: an overgrown path through the woods that went along a creek. Here I slowed down, coasted through the green shade, and scanned the brownish water. I'd never seen any fish in the creek. I knew there were fish here, somewhere, searching the scoured bottom for pockets of gravel, craters in the granite riverbed that still held little stones, places where they could hide their eggs in the voids between pebbles. Out of the corner of my eye I saw a long shadow peel off the shade along the far bank, bolt for a riffle, and disappear. I stopped, tried to see it, and listened to the creek. Nothing came of it. Five minutes later I emerged, chilled by the water-cooled shade of the bike path, behind my apartment building.

"MAXIMUM CAPACITY OF THESE SHELVES IS TEN standard packages. Don't try to fit more on there. They won't fit. Don't squish the packages.

"The label should go here. Parallel with the others. Not wonky.

"Nobody likes it wonky. This isn't an art store, get that?"

Elevator humming.

"In a moment we'll be on the ground floor, where the customers are. Once you're on the ground floor, you're in the eye of the shopper. You represent the company. There's a certain way you must walk when you're on the ground floor, a certain expression you must be wearing on your face at all times, a certain lack of wrinkles in your shirt where it's tucked into your pants. Understand?"

WHEN I GOT HOME I FOUND BOB sitting at the kitchen table smoking and drawing. He didn't look up from his work. The recycling bin was overflowing and I started pulling out pages, blooming the crumples, and watching the back of Bob's head to see if he would react to the noise.

"Bob, these are great," I said.

I made a pile of the drawings he'd thrown away, opened a couple of beers for us, and sat next to him at the table. I put my arm around his waist and kissed him on his pink-flushed cheek. I was enough bigger than he that I had to be careful with affection. Bob ashed and blew smoke.

"And how was filling the bins today? Did you keep them brimming for the customers?"

"I did."

"You're cold."

"It's hotter than hell in here."

"You're sucking the heat from the room."

"I know it. They had me work in frozen today."

"They're trying to freeze you solid," Bob said, and handed me his smoke. "Breathe it in. Breathe deep. I'm going to cook you something spicy."

"You don't have to do that. You should keep working."

"Go get changed and jump rope for a while. I'll make us food."

I got on the rope and worked heat back into me. Bob watched and drew. Rice was steaming up the kitchen. Bob lit another smoke. He'd smoke two at once if he could pull it off. Moths flew in and out of the steam like planes in the clouds. The little pot on its electric coil rattled in rhythm with my footfalls. The neighbor pounded on the wall.

"Don't worry about it," Bob said, "Louie cried all day. Keep jumping rope."

I stopped jumping, took a drink of my beer, and looked at the wall through which the sound had come. Bob had a red pencil in his hand and was shading my face. He drew a halo of heat around my ribs.

"Is he saying anything yet?" I said.

"Not really."

"Did you see Kiki today?"

"I went over and played with Louie for an hour so she could go to the welfare office."

"Did she actually go this time?"

"No."

I jumped rope and Bob drew me. I started telling him about the Big Man—how that was actually the name of a person: the boss of the GoBig store. Every morning at six o'clock he would come in from the parking lot, his pale skin husked in a starched, white shirt pulled so tight you could see his nipples. The Big Man came in and strolled the aisles, beginning with the bakery and moving on to the bulk: one of each, one of each, one of each. He stopped, sniffed, and took notes in a spiral-bound pad he kept in his chest pocket. Bob crumpled up the picture he was working on and threw it in the corner. I stopped jumping. Through the wall I heard Louie laugh.

WE MET KIKI AND LOUIE ON THE day Kiki decided to have a yard sale. I'd been working at GoBig for about a week, and already knew that I wouldn't last. That morning, Bob and I walked out the door and saw that someone's apartment had been blown out across the shared lawn. Half the junk was covered in sequins. Beside a sequined jumpsuit a scratched pan lay overturned in the grass. By a dandelion was a gallon ziploc stuffed with old coupons. Kiki and Bob bonded over the sequins; he could bond with anybody. His new thing was dressing up in gaudy costumes and then posting photos of himself on the web. I poked through the stuff on the lawn for a while and then, when I looked back, Bob was gone. I eventually found him inside Kiki's apartment, which appeared still to be full of trinkets past-capacity. Her shelves were sagging beneath the weight of her decorations. She had Bob face-down on the living-room floor and was sitting on top of him. *"Energy work,"* she said to me. In the corner, inside a plastic castle, Louie worked on Mr. Potato Head. When I tried to talk to him he just looked through me, as if he were wondering where I'd fit as a piece. I couldn't help it—I felt terrible about this—but he scared me. Bob's little sister was autistic, so he'd taken to Louie without thinking.

"Why does he make you so uncomfortable?" Bob asked me once. We were sitting on the stoop watching cars go by and drinking 40s when Kiki walked up with Louie slung over her shoulder. He wasn't asleep and was too big to be on her shoulder. His eyes were locked on me as Kiki slid him through her door.

"He doesn't make me uncomfortable."

"You don't have to be ashamed. I'm not gonna judge you," Bob said, frowning.

"No, I know that. It's just that he doesn't make me uncomfortable."

WHILE BOB AND I ATE SPICY RICE we heard a knock on the door. I got up to answer it while Bob watched from his seat at the table. Outside, Kiki waited on the stoop looking down at her glittering toenails and shifting her feet so they were safely away from cracks. Then she looked up, over my shoulder, searching for Bob.

"Hello, Kiki," I said.

"Hi."

"What's up?"

"Bob home?"

Kiki stepped into the door frame and I was forced to back up. Half her hair was tucked into a leopard-print top, like she'd just slid it on, and the rest of it was in the claws of a jeweled barrette.

"Bob?" Kiki crooned.

"Hi, Kiki. You bring it?" Bob said from the table.

"Yeah, here it is." She held something in her hands, something plastic and pastel blue with an antenna.

"Just leave it with him. We're in the middle of dinner. See you when you get back," Bob said.

"Oh. Okay." Kiki frowned. She handed me the plastic receiver.

"You gonna be up for a while?" she said across my shoulder.

"Dunno. Probably," Bob said.

"Maybe we could hang out when I get back. Have a drink maybe?"

"We'll see."

"Bye, Kiki," I said, and began to close the door. Kiki was begging Bob with her eyes, completely unashamed. I shut the door and locked the deadbolt.

"Poor girl," I said, and sat down on Bob's lap.

"Today she showed me her unicorn collection," he said, "and then told me about this baby monitor. I'm supposed to listen and make sure Louie doesn't have a meltdown while she's gone."

"You're doing what? Bob, she's obsessed with you. Doesn't she know you're—"

"I go there for Louie."

I stood up and kissed Bob on his head. I cleaned a pot in the sink then stared above the backsplash. An old pastel of us was once taped to the wall there. Over time the water had gotten to it, then Bob took it down and hadn't replaced it.

"Does she think we're brothers or something?"

"No," he said. I stared at the dirty wall. It was too quiet.

I COULDN'T SLEEP. BOB LAY SNORING BESIDE me. Thoughts of my day at GoBig crept into my mind and I tried to banish them. Work started in five hours. Voices from GoBig flowed through my head, bringing me back to the labyrinth of junk food.

"Be careful when you use your box cutter. Plan your incision before removing it when you're on the ground floor. Nobody wants to see you hanging out with a blade in your hand like you're looking for something to cut with it. The large bags are properly cut at the corner, average slice length four inches, and the incision should be made once the top of the bin has been removed—not before. If you do it wrong you'll spill product everywhere. If you create a spill, your creation of that spill will be noted along with the time you made it, where you did it, and how much you spilled. This data will be sent to the men in accounting and they will plug it into the Termination Determinate Algorithm, or TAD. It's not up to us. It's up to the TAD. Nothing personal; it's just that this is a big company. The customers love this company, and they're the ones who pay our wages. It's critical that you understand that part. Company policy is to report a spill immediately, as soon as you see it. The reports have been incentivized in such a way that your co-workers will definitely report that it was you they saw making the spill as opposed to covering for you by saying it was a customer. Again, nothing personal. It's just that we've found this system works."

"I understand clearly. Spill reports," I said.

The manager shifted papers around on his desk.

"Do you have a family?"

Silence. Shrug. Mouth lolls open.

"Good job on the bolognas, by the way. Most people fuck that up."

Silence. Wave of euphoria. Self-loathing.

Bob rolled over and threw a leg over me. The baby monitor on our bedside table chirped, then a wave of static came up in volume. I heard Louie breathing, then the sound of a door slamming, then Kiki's voice. I turned off the monitor. Trying to catch sleep, I thought about the creek. I pictured the fish, got eye-to-eye with it under the water. I thought about how I'd been trying to find a gravel pocket in the streambed somewhere, a still place beneath the current for me and Bob, and I realized how I hadn't, and that I was losing hope.

IN THE MORNING, AT WORK, I WITNESSED a spill. First I heard the sound of whimpering, then, following it, I arrived at the scene.

"Javier!" I whispered.

"Go away," he said, crouching in front of the Cosmic Corn bulk bin. A galaxy of silver-dipped popcorn kernels was spilled all around him. Between sobs, he scooped kernels off the floor with a little plastic shovel and slid them back into the bag. More kernels spilled out each time he did this. He was swearing at himself in Spanish and smacking himself on the forehead with his palm.

An hour and a half later I was in the floor manager's office. He swiveled his chair as he spoke, fingers linked behind his head, shirt cuffs rolled past his elbows. I caught sight of the thing I'd heard about, there on his bicep: he and the other managers had matching GoBig tattoos.

"So how are things going for you?"

"Fine," I said, "I'm feeling good about it."

"Good about it? Good about what?"

"The job, I mean, the training."

"You think it's going well? That's good to hear," he said.

He leaned forward. His fingertips touched their twins in a steeple between his eyes.

"So tell me what happened earlier," he said.

"What do you mean?"

"I mean with Javier. His fuck-up."

"Oh. Well, I was stocking and then I saw that he had spilled."

"You saw that he had spilled the gummy bears on the floor."

"Yes. The kettle corn was what was spilled, adjacent to the gummy bears. I was stocking the sugar when I heard it, then I went to see what had happened."

"Well hey, you're not in trouble. Don't act so nervous."

"I'm not nervous."

"Not nervous?"

"No."

"Why should you be? I mean, Javier was the one who spilled and he's gone now. And seriously, I mean, between me and you, who didn't see it coming, right?"

Silence.

"Did you get time to fill out a spill report?" he said.

"No, I—"

"You know you are required by company policy to fill out a spill report following a spill and you've been on the clock for two hours since the accident and, still, you haven't even *begun* to fill out a report?"

"To be honest, I thought Ned might have done it. I mean, he found the spill maybe ten seconds after I did, so I assumed—"

"Assumed?"

Silence. Stomach drops out.

"All right. It's no big deal this time. We like you. You're on time, you do a fine job, and you're polite. One more thing though, before you go. Ned said you were you laughing when he came over. Why were you laughing?"

I SAT IN KIKI'S APARTMENT WATCHING CANDLES drip wax down colored-glass bottles. Mobiles hung from the ceiling, beautiful ornaments Bob and Louie had made together. Every inch of counter space was filled with some kind of trinket, but nothing that could be fit into the mouth and swallowed. Kiki kept her knives in a locked drawer and kept the little key on a necklace where it hung beside a dried raven's foot and a whistle. The candles were placed high enough so Louie couldn't reach the flames and had stained the ceiling with soot. Books were everywhere: books about ayurveda, Amazon wizards, mystic tarot, spirit communication, the gifted child... When Kiki spoke, her voice came low and rapid. I could barely ever hear her, though I knew she often talked louder—when Bob was there and I'd stayed home, for instance. All the food in Kiki's house was kept in the fridge, including the cereal, so that the mice couldn't get to it. Kiki took a deep drink from a quart of beer and stirred a pot of cooked macaroni that was starting to smoke on the stove.

"Kee—turn down the food," Bob yelled from across the room. He sat watching cartoons with Louie, recordings on a VHS tape they kept rewinding so they could go over the same scenes.

"What?" Kiki said.

"The flame, Bob's saying it's too hot," I said. I was sitting near Kiki, working on my drink. When I'd gotten home from work the apartment had been empty. I could hear Bob and Louie through the wall, then Kiki talking about something in an enthusiastic, annoying voice. Frustration rippled through me. I'd gone over to see what was up. When I got there, Kiki acted like I was her and Bob's dad coming in to bring down the hammer. She was nervous. I made myself friendly. Kiki had been texting Bob more and more lately; I knew that because he complained about it. He could complain about her for an hour one night and then be over at her house when I got home the next. It seemed he was spending more time doing art with Louie than working seriously on his own pieces. He'd begun a huge canvas three months earlier but now the thing sat half-done on an easel in our living room. He hadn't touched it in weeks.

Now his art was for Louie. If he was doing art, he was doing it because of Louie. The burnt macaroni was for Louie. Louie was the only one who finished his bowl of it, and wouldn't have if it weren't for the heaping tablespoon of peanut butter Kiki slipped into it with her finger. Peach fuzz had begun to appear above Louie's lip. He looked around the table, grinning, with a mouthload of macaroni for us to watch. The boy was all joy until

Bob and I got up to leave. Then he cried, and on top of it Kiki acted hurt that we were going. My last glimpse of Kiki was her leaning against the kitchen counter with hair in front of her face, candlelight on her gold sequins, and the can in her hand, Louie latched at her knees, bawling.

IT WAS DARK AND HOT. TOO HOT to sleep. A train whistle blew in the distance. Bob was snoring and had stolen all the sheets so I lay there in my underwear, sweating. The AC at work had screwed with my skin thickness. A pain began pulsing in a rear molar and then the thought came that I'd soon be paying for its extraction. I pulled hard on the covers but Bob had them locked tight in his arms. The baby monitor fuzzed a mist of sound, and now and then a babble. I pictured Louie tossing and turning in a crib too small for him. I should go out and find Kiki, get her a ride home from wherever she was, pull her off the karaoke mike or yank the pool cue from her hand and throw her in the back of a car. She was probably wearing a wig. She was probably wearing a wig and fucking someone in a pool-hall bathroom. Kiki's voice came through the baby monitor.

"*Bob,*"

I froze. Kiki breathed heavily into the other end of the monitor.

"*Bob. Please, Bob, come over. Bob, please. I gotta talk to you.*"
Silence. Stomach drops out.

I got out of bed and picked up the monitor, threw on a robe. I watched Bob half wake up, then roll over and throw his leg across where I'd just been.

KIKI STOOD IN HER DOORWAY, matching my gaze without an ounce of fear visible. She was actually smiling at me: the sweaty guy with bedhead and robe, baby monitor in hand like a dead animal, in the hall at three in the morning.

"Hi," she said.

"Thought you might want this back," I said, handing her the monitor.

"Thanks a lot," she said, and took the monitor. "I can't thank Bob enough, I mean, for helping with Louie. Louie would just die without him, you know. He's never had a dad before."

Kiki was slurring her words. A smell of incense billowed from inside. The place was lit with only candles. I couldn't think of what to say. Nothing I could do would penetrate.

"You don't have to leave," Kiki said. "Wanna stay for a drink? I could fix you something to eat. I don't want to be rude. Is Bob awake? Maybe he wants to—"

"Bob's asleep. It's three in the morning."

"Oh."

"I gotta be at work in four hours. Good night."

She was still watching me when I opened the door of our apartment. Her head was hanging out of her doorway, and she was waving to me. I didn't wave back.

AT WORK I WAS TRAPPED IN A way that Louie could never be. Two whole pallets of hot dogs came through the swinging doors one day in July. I hung package after package of hot dogs on their cold, metal hangers—hung them by the tiny hole punched in the plastic flap at the top. I hung the packages until my arms grew tired, I got sloppy, and one of them exploded. Odorless packing juice sprayed across the front of my uniform and onto the floor. I walked to the spill kit dripping hot-dog water but someone had beaten me to it. The floor manager held the intercom to his ear and spoke into the phone.

CLEANUP AISLE TWELVE. WET FLOOR HAZARD. I REPEAT: CLEANUP AISLE TWELVE. WET FLOOR HAZARD.

If Bob were there he would have made the manager into a big old log, I'd be wearing plaid and suspenders, I'd have a barrel-thick chest and an axe in my hand. As usual, I was glad he wasn't there so that he couldn't see what happened in reality.

WHEN I GOT HOME I FOUND CRAYON drawings littering the apartment. Louie was in the kitchen, face down on the floor, and Bob was on top of him. A peaceful kind of music I hadn't heard before was coming through our speakers, and Bob was giving Kiki's energy therapy to Louie. When he saw me, Louie said, "He's home early!," and that was the first time, so Bob keeps telling me, that he'd ever really spoken.

STEVE KRONEN

Croatoan

FOR MY DAUGHTER

Later that afternoon, home for summer, she de-shines
her nose, does her eyes with the risen (plucked) brows
and steady gaze portrait painters
give to distance and perspective and the parallel lines
that vanish beyond the field mapped out on the canvas—
dabbing here and there, dabbing here in the house
where her bed is which sprawled like a savannah once
and is contracted now to bed-size. It contains her

own sprawling self when she comes in late out of the milkman's
dark, a dark now without milkmen, or milkmen's hours,
passenger pigeons, dodos, Roanoke, Judge Crater—done in
all by tooth, claw, entropy, greed, brigands on the Silk
Road, vertigo, wind. In my rear-view mirror
the hedge of her campus flowers
reduced itself to her signature, a pink lipstick smear
on the bathroom mirror, "Kronen," perhaps, or "Croatoan."

Realms of Old

FOR MY WIFE ON HER 51ST BIRTHDAY

When the elevator's lifting one
toward some upper story,
admire the scene at 51.

Such a promontory
allows, 360 round,
rivers, hills, and fissures,

and, boundaries unbound,
no landscape's cut with scissors
of a small and youthful disregard

into abbreviated segments
but yard leads unto yard
and pigments merge with pigments,

all the roads and mazes
that baffled at street level
occasions now for praises,

though you are hushed with marvel—
not the silence of some stout Cortez
whose eagle-eye would conquer all,

but amusement for what is,
the distances grown tranquil
and, destinations halved—

not Achilles and his tortoise
or a cloth each night unweaved—
but, footstep or by Otis,

as in your tattered Homer,
your every Troy and Panama
is carried with you homeward—

here—your eyes my panorama.

This Is How

Hitler himself giving it only a thousand years, the empire
he'd fashioned with his artist hands from majestic Black Forest
   wood

and the Holy Roman Empire and the pumps and brogans
heaped on tables and the carbon married smartly

to molten iron mined for centuries from the Ruhr Valley
where Arminius trashed Varus's three startled legions, and then,

no more. All things,
the poisoned little bellows of his heart admitted,

collapse at last upon themselves.
"How," my mother asked once in the hall-lit kitchen,

holding up the cleanly halved plate in her two spotted hands,
"did this happen?" Her pupils were large. *"How?"*

When Lord Kelvin, computing the life-span
of the sun, calculating the time needed

for its thrashing center to release
its gravitational energy, tick down and cool, he gave it

thirty million years. How imprecise his tools and how vast
the ignorance of 1862. The sun, we know now, will shine

for seven billion years. *"How,"* she demanded,
her terror growing in her throat, *"how, how?"*

TADEUSZ DĄBROWSKI

TRANSLATED BY ANTONIA LLOYD-JONES

Nothing Was Made

Hudson 2013

Here, where roe deer, black bears, squirrels, and boar full
of eyes in front and behind go running across your
bedclothes, where you restlessly pace the length of superstores
that look forward to seeing you twenty-four hours a day,
ready to sell you six gallons of beer, a three-pound
bag of chips for two, a "party box" of condoms
in the largest size, a Batman costume deceptively
similar to the original, and even a night
shirt shaped like a rasher of bacon; where cars
as big as combines harvest your dream of escaping
into the backwoods, along with wild brutes and brutalized
people; where while surfing channels you take the measure of time,
successive arousing and settings of the sun, you meet women
with tattoos on their irises and souls like Nagasaki
(following contact with the Fat Man) or the latest iPhone;
right here, half-way through your life—for you're always
half-way through—you suddenly hear the prices freeze,
the bellies of fridges and vagrants cease to rumble,
tumors and politicians no longer feel like multiplying
the obvious, the dead aren't anxious about their bank balance
standing in line for the cashier, tattoos erupt in the sky,
which closes its blind eye to the high jinks
of clouds and teenagers in student dorms, the assassin's
bullet hangs in mid-air and is not yet
lethal, a thought solidifying between synapses. And right here
poetry appears, and forces a stag to bolt
in front of the hood of your car, bids an apple break free

of its branch, the light to burgeon and burst the shell
of the night, a husband to think of his wife while
masturbating, airplanes to fly to, and ramblers to walk to their
     goal,
God to perform a few miracles, the liar to win another
election, the religious poet to write some good
verse. Nobody saw it. But without it, nothing was made
that was made.

The Gargantuan City

gorges itself and fattens,
and then dreams it's breaking records for burning
calories at a fitness club.

The city shudders deliriously
whenever the subway goes by. It howls with pain when there's a
snarl-up in its arteries.

It shits itself, but
tries hard to clean up the mess. It drools at the sight
of soaking wet girls in T-shirts.

It is moved
at the thought of the art it preserves
in its sieve-like memory.

It always lies
on one side, that's why it likes to feel millions of micro-
organisms moving inside it.

The city believes
it will remain young forever, though that's not at all
what it wants. It longs for someone

to disconnect it from the drip.
But that's not possible, because its body has gained
self-consciousness.

By night from an airplane
it looks like Nero's burning Rome. Or else
a tumor on a CAT scan. Or an eye,

its iris encrypted with
yearning.

Shadows

TO THE WINOS OF BERLIN

sneaking across the park at night, sleeping
under plastic like rotten cauliflowers. Nematodes
crawling out of sewers, creeping along
in the bowels of the nightly subway. Distinguishing marks without
properties, down-and-out sources of shame, acet-
aldehydes. Hackneyed words on the rasping
tongues of escalators, identity cards
without owners, numbers, or photos. O human clay,
which crumbles under the boot of frost. I pay homage to
Your Helplessnesses, your amnesias, and your
mental diarrhea. You make your pilgrimage to earth
more consciously and with greater passion than I do.
Soon the water will evaporate from you and fall in clean
rain on the heads of passers-by from the Champs Elysées,
Fifth Avenue, the Ku'damm, onto their clean consciences.
Onto clean sand.

MATT ZAMBITO

Thou Shalt Not "Off" Thyself

Don't get fancy on me, my siblings. Don't dress up
like an old buck and lumber the woods
come hunting season's start. Don't gobble
yolk-only omelets just to jack up the chance

for a heart attack. I'll stop. Joking is to *felo-de-se*
as a rodeo clown is to animal rights.
Christmas will come, Christmas will pass. Flood,
divorce, misfired pills, that terrible thing you did—

life will chase you down, it's true. I know. It says,
Hate the sinner, love the sin. It says, *I'm not trying
to be nice.* It says, *I'm not that nice.* The brain
is the city and the land outside the city soaking up

its own rivers of sludge. The brain holds the heart,
arms, mitochondria—the whole enchilada
of a body—hostage with its hegemony. I know:
I've held a blade to my throat ready

in my head but not my marrow. I know:
I've dangled from a rope in my black dog's loyal
reveries. But in my dreams, I've never thought
I'd be reduced to dust by neurons gone wrong. Like me,

you can't receive reasons to breathe
other than these: There's more to do than death
allows the world; and this world,
our sentient machine, deserves less death, more you.

AARON THIER

Mr. Eternity

1560

First I was only an Indian. I was a Pirahao girl from the city of Anaquitos, which the Christians call El Dorado. My mother was dead and no one said anything about her, and then my father was dead also and I was sold to the traders on the river. I was loaded into a canoe with the dyewood, the brazil nuts, the bundles of dried monkey meat, the flying dog wool, the rubber toys. I was sent down the river to the city of Omagua, and then to another city, and then to another. Then I arrived here, in the small Christian city of Santa Ines, in the New Kingdom of Granada, where the Pirahao river plows into the Caribbean sea. The ocean does not exist in Pirahao, and I could not see it until I learned to say the word in Spanish. I was a slave and then, because I am so beautiful that men become drunk when they look at me, I was sold to the Senora at the brothel and I became a whore.

Now I am both an Indian and a Christian. When I'm asleep my name is Xiako and I speak Pirahao and nothing exists that can't be seen. When I'm asleep I want to return to Anaquitos and live as I did, among people and not among Christians. But when I'm awake I speak Spanish and God watches us from his heaven and my name is Maria. When I'm awake I know about vengeance and I want the Christians to destroy Anaquitos as they are said to have destroyed Tenochtitlan and the cities of Tahuantinsuyu. I want the Pirahao to die and I want them to know they are dying because of me, because they sold me like a rubber toy, because they took my life from me when I was small and alone.

At the brothel I meet soldiers and clerks and notaries and I tell them stories about Anaquitos so they will hate that place as much as I do. I say that the king and queen have regal titles so long that one lifetime isn't long enough to speak them in their entirety. I say that they only eat human flesh. I say that they make drums from human skin, and they make necklaces from human teeth, and from the skulls they make the ceremonial cups from which they drink manioc beer. I say that they pray to the mountains, which are their gods. Sometimes I laugh when I tell these stories. The soldiers are horrified by this. My stories are true in Spanish, in which everything is true, but they are not true in Pirahao. There are no gods in Pirahao. There are no kings and queens.

I can say whatever I like because the Christians believe in everything, even things they don't believe in, even things that don't exist. They tell me that everything they do is done in the service of God. There is no other god but God, and God is three gods, all of whom are the same, and there are many other gods also. Some gods exist and some do not. There is Maria, the mother god, who gave me her name. There are the saints and virgins and angels and there is the devil, Satan, who lives in the world beneath the world. There are so many gods that they are like the insects that scatter when a rotting log is disturbed, although none is as important as God himself, whom the Christians thank for every bee sting and fear more than anything else, more than Satan, more than death, more than the worst pain. In Spanish, it is because of God that the world exists. In Pirahao there are only things that exist, and the world, like things, exists for no reason.

For the Christians it is a sin to eat pineapple before taking communion. It is a sin to change the bed linens on Friday. It is a sin to say that fornication with an Indian is no sin. However, it is not a sin to fornicate with an Indian. This is an enigma and a mystery of the Faith and the result is that many Christian officials have Indian concubines, although they do not say so. One afternoon two soldiers bring me to the alcalde mayor's official residence and I become a concubine myself. This is very fortunate. It is easier to be the alcalde's concubine than it is to be a whore, not only because the alcalde is a kind man, always trying to be better and do honor to God, always affirming that Indians are true human beings and not simply beasts, always fretting and worrying in his anguish for salvation, but also because his appetites are depraved and he never touches me. His intention is to disguise his real desires, which have to do with animals, with young pigs, not piglets but young adult pigs. He does not touch the pigs either. He does not even touch himself. He stands in the pigpen and prays to God, poor man, and he mourns the fact of his desire.

I live very well in the alcalde's house. I drink cashew wine until I am so stupid I forget my Christian name. I eat guava paste and porpoise pepper steak and sea bird eggs. No one bothers me. When I need something I steal it from the alcalde or lie down with one of the guards at the residence. But my life is not my own. No one listens to me and I have no power to make things happen. I think of the Pirahao in their white city and my anger is a thing I can hold in my hand.

And then one day I see an opportunity. One day a wrinkled conquistador in a red Toledo cap comes walking out of the forest. His name is Daniel de Fo and he is one hundred years old and he is the only survivor of the Lopez y Barra expedition to the land of cinnamon, which is what the Christians call the inland forest through which the Pirahao river flows. The Senora gives him a room at the brothel and he sleeps for three days, and I am there visiting friends when he wakes up and begins to speak of a city in the forest.

Daniel de Fo can't tell his story without speaking heresies. He says, "There are things in the forest that not even God knows about. An ant bit my foot off, or he bit me and then my friend had to cut the foot off, but it was fine because the Indians had a medicine to make it grow back."

The soldiers put their hands over his mouth. They say this is witchcraft and they won't let him damn himself by talking about it. They won't let themselves hear the story. But he doesn't care. He laughs and laughs, a sound like haha. I don't care either because I know that in Anaquitos this medicine exists. I know that he has been there. I know that he wants to go back. I can see the web of God's design shining in the sea light.

In Pirahao, the truth is only what happens and time is an animal that sleeps all day. In Spanish, the truth is whatever a woman tells her gods, a different story every day, and time is a river in which she struggles to stay afloat. When I speak Pirahao, I want to return to the city and eat inaga fruit in the central plaza, but when I speak Spanish I want to see the city burn, and it is only in Spanish that it's proper to act. It is this difference that dooms the Pirahao.

1750

I have liv'd upon this *Nauseous Orb* the Earth for near seventie years, and to day, the principal actors in my life's Drama being dead (except I imagine Dr. Dan Defoe who will outlive us all), and accordingly unable, if I judge rightly the termes conditions of the *Afterlife*, to bring a Suit against me, I perceive the time is ripe to tell the adventures and misventures of my life, for tho I am now Resident in Boston, city of snows and fogs, yet my memory capers among the palmy green islands of youth.

I shall tell my story from front to back—I shall pour it out scum and sediment and all—for it wants nothing, and requires nothing of the *Artificers Art*. I was born in the Barbados, and there I was inured to hardship and cruel treatment, but in the year 1750, when I was a young man of nineteen years, I fled from there to the Bahama islands and sought to raise myself by an audacious deception, as I will shortly explain.

In the Bahamas I traveled from one house to the next, the guest of all, and from one island to the next, pass'd as it were from hand to hand among the debased gentry of that piratical country, who were all of them second sons bastard sons spalpeens and barrowers raised to the peerage, and I received as hearty a welcome as ever I could have wished. One day I came to stop with Mr. Galsworthy of Babylon plantation, upon an island called Little Salt. As it was then after noon, and his custom to feed without stint or measure each day at two o'clock, or three, I dress'd quickly in the best of what I had and came down to meet my host at table, including many other guests. It was here I spied for the first time Daniel Defoe, whom they call'd the Spaynard, an old man like a hat-stand with eyes, or a scarecrow totteringly put together, or a jointed insect in a wig, acclaim'd by popular belief to be near three hundred years of age.

The great house at Babylon was poorly constructed, in grate haste, namely that some rooms were walled with grave markers, and others with a kind of white washed dung. I think this were not for want of credit or capital, but only that Mr. Galsworthy did so enjoy a sumptuous table that his only thought was for feasting, and all the rest were bagatelles and trifles. In this he was like the man who gambles his estate for a thrill, or sells the cloathes off his back for the taste and quickness of wine. To-day we dined upon stew'd mudfish, pickled crabs, roast pig, roast yam, plantanes, boil'd pudding, roast coot, water milions, and many other fuds viz. doves ducks fishes. For my part I worked at a ham the size of a cloak-bag.

Yet soon our revelry was interrupted by the visitation of brooding death. One of the guests, a Mr. Foster, gave a small scream and, stiff and benumb'd, though also it seemed in excruciating pain, endeavored to rise, which task being impossible he next grobled about for whatever chanced to be within his reach, snatching the wig from his companion's head, and then, giving another scream, slipped forward dead with his face in his fud. We now all gazed about uncertain what to do, for if Mr. Foster had been poisoned, as it did appear he had been, (which was not unusual in the Bahamas at that time, where the slaves did frequently season their masters fud with corrosive sublimate), then I expected our next concern would be to torment slave after slave until we had learnt the culprits. Daniel Defoe no doubt thought as I did, and not wishing to see this feast spoilt, for it was a good one, nor indeed any slaves tormented, he knelt by the dead man, grabbed hold of his cheeks, looked in his mouth, lifted his hand and let it fall, listened at his chest, and then, without canvassing the matter any further, pronounced him dead not of poyson but from a surfeit of Pig.

Now we were at ease once more, this occurrence being nothing remarkable in such a place, where death blew through every big house like a *summer breeze*. Only those guests newly arriv'd from England were alarmed, and stared about, their faces *masks* of *horror*. Mr. Galsworthy for his part was delighted to discover in Daniel Defoe, called from that point *Doctor* Dan, a person with some knowledge of medicine, and pressed him now with questions and concerns of all sorts, asking whether a surfeit of duck mite produce a similar outcome, or of crab, and if not was there some Fatal Characteristic peculiar to the pig.

I settl'd in to listen, drinking punch & gazing at the slaves, who moved about clearing dishes. I knew from their faces they had poisoned Mr. Foster, though I ne'er learnt the reason.

Dr. Dan answered that a surfeit of pig sometimes produced what was called by physicians a coagluation of the *Gluten* or some say *Animal mixt*, which retarded obstructed the circulation of the blood. A surfeit of any animal fud will produce the same outcome in any other animal, but the calamity proceeds quick or slow according to the degree of relationship between the animal consum'd to the animal which consumes it, for ex. a man must eat more duck to produce the same fatal coagluation, but a much smaller amount of monkey, and still less of Ape, Sphinx, or Satyr, which of all animals are mans closest cousins. Cannibalism that heathen rite is known to produce an *instantaneous* coagluation. However, said Dr. Dan, remember that a duck is safer eating the meat of a Human than if he eats the meat of his own cousin and near relation, the goose.

Notwithstanding he spoke with authoritie I knew him for an imposter, yet I said nothing, for I recognized him as *one oozy worm recognizes another* though neither have the use of reason. Here I was at table to every appearance a white man among white men, yet I was a sheep in wolf's clothing after all. You see dear reader my father was Mr. Coleman of Elizabeth plantation in the Barbados, that is God's truth, yet my mother was his *Slave*, named Liberty, which made me neither one thing nor another, but surely no gentleman. In the Bahama islands I called myself John Green, and have done ever since.

2500

My father was the hereditary king and president of the Democratic Federation of Mississippi States, which was lucky for him because he loved the amenities of power and the exercise of governance. It was not so lucky for the people he ruled over, however, nor for the country at large, which ultimately disappeared away into the lavender light and sweet scented dust of history. But that is putting the car before the hearse.

Originally, our dominions comprised St. Louis, where we lived, and most of the land west to Kansas City and south to the first wild reaches of the Mississippi jungle, which in truth made it not Mississippi states, as the country's name boldly stated, but only the one individual old state of Missouri with some drips and drops of Arkansas. As for ourselves, we remained in St. Louis at all times. I recollect it as a city of almost twenty-five thousand souls, a city of date palms and mud houses and banana beer, and it was hot enough to fry an ape most of the time, except January and February. It was my family's home for centuries.

Our name is Roulette, but I am Jasmine St. Roulette, the St. part having been added for a hint of style. I was the only issue of my father's union with a mystery mother whom I never knew, and therefore our presidential family consisted of only two members, although the household was augmented tenfold by servants and slaves, and days might pass when I did not see my father at all, or saw him only at official occasions. We lived extravagantly in our hereditary palace, which had once been the city library of imperial St. Louis. We had an oven big enough to bake fifty cassava rounds at one time. We had baths as big as a farmer's whole house. We had a hundred peacocks, acrylic clothing, real carpets, paraffin lanterns, plastic bins and jugs, and exotic commodities like cashew wine, which we obtained from neighboring countries on an economy of exchange. We had water tanks and strategic grain reserves, and the whole edifice was encapsulated from the poor people within an enormous concrete wall.

For me, however, life was corrupted by frustrations, because I was a woman in a place and time where men hoarded up all the power. I could never participate in the larger sphere of activity. My father used me like a bartering chip. He affianced me to a sequence of men, the last of whom was the piggish senator Anthony Fucking Corvette, whom I had to visit each week to solidify family alliances. We would sit together at an antique plastic table and he would say things like, "It is better to drink muddy water and eat dirt." Better than what? Then I had to let him do it to me. He did it by rote and political requirement and then he bollocked off to his hookers and his poppy juice and I went home to lie in my hammock and dream of another life. This is what it was to be a president's daughter in the final years of the twenty-fifth century. It was an endless liturgy of palace tedium and an injustice of diminished freedoms. I called myself an anachro-feminist, a term of my own proud coinage, but it was only a phrase. I had no recourse.

My father did not care a sesame seed for my troubles, but we did share one fascination in common, which was the transformations and legacies of history. We had only a limited selection of books in the palace, but we knew which side the world was buttered on. We knew that we were opulent people in an impoverished time. We knew that our country was just a subsistence nation of millet and goats and camels. The ruins of great days fringed and ringed the city in a huge periphery and we knew that our own St. Louis was only a tiny particle of the St. Louis that had existed in ancient bygone imperial days. The difference was that while I sat in the library striving to learn all I could about the true and established facts of the world, my father hardly read anything anymore, and instead he preoccupied himself with thoughts of his own place in history. His great ambition was to unite all the nations of North America under one flag, as they'd been united in freedom and democracy under the empire of the United States. He also wanted to revitalize culture and learning. I often heard him say things like, "It is time we remodernized this ragbag old country."

He had mandated that we speak only Modern English at home, the language of American scholars, and I wasn't allowed to speak Mississippi Spanish at all until I was ten years old, but other than this he did nothing, for he didn't know how to commence the effort of remodernization. Maybe, in an alternative reality, he would never have been catalyzed into action at all, but it happened that one night, when I myself was already twenty-six and my father had long since begun to feel the pinch of years, he bought an old slave named Daniel Defoe from some people who came in off the desert. It was a night of shining rain and cicadas, which I know because I chanced to be there. I was just returning from dinner and fornications with Anthony Fucking Corvette, and my father was out by the front gate, and when he saw me he said, "Oh, it's you," as if he had just recollected my existence. "Then come along and I'll show you something."

We issued into the camel pen and there was Daniel Defoe. It was the first time I cast eyes on him. He had a superannuated cat named Christopher Smart, who was like a grey carpet with teeth, and he was handsome and there were lights in his eyes, but his chief appeal and the reason for my father's interest in him was that he was said to be one thousand years old. This was not impossible if you considered that he came from the desert. In very dry air, with abundant sun, meat will cure before it spoils, and therefore a human being, which is made of meat, could theoretically live forever. The marked contrast was that in St. Louis, which was frequently ravaged by pestilences like Nevada fever, even rich people lived only fifty or sixty years. Poor people were lucky to survive into their thirties.

"If he's as old as he says," my father instructed, "he would have known the glory of the United States."

He was speaking Modern English, and it was an astonishment when Daniel Defoe responded in the same language. His accent was untraceable. He said, "Don't talk to me about glory. Those people were out of their minds. They only cared about whale oil. They lived in tents called wigwams. Their method of gardening was to explode chemical bombs, which killed everything."

My father said, "We know about oil. We have books and prospectuses in the palace." But I knew he had not read a prospectus in years.

"It wasn't only whale oil. It was fossilized oil too. They pumped it out of the earth and drank it like it was banana beer. They pumped so much out of the ground that the land began to sink, and that's why it seemed like the seas were rising. They also made a special train oil from the fat of a seabird called the great auk, which was the national bird of the United States. Train oil made the economy boom, but it also caused global warming because it released all the heat that would otherwise have stayed inside the auks, which were arctic birds, and very warm inside, and anyway extremely numerous."

This was not true. It was a feast of lies. However, my father devoured it, and I think this marked the sea change for him. He had lacked an advisor to ratify and affirm his ideas. Now he had one.

"We've got to find some of these great auks," he said quietly. "We won't burn so many to cause global warming. Only enough to make our economy boom."

IN THE EARLY STAGES OF THE remodernization campaign, before everything dried up and blew away in bundles of tinder and chaff, there was an idyll of repose. It was the winding of a watch. My own routine continued unimpeded, with few palpable changes. I got up early, when the heat started to rise, and breakfasted on the roof in the cool morning air. I had cold cornmeal porridge as well as mango, a little yoga cream, and a cup of hot caffeine. Then I persecuted my education. First, while my brain was still soft, I read my Modern English history books, and later I had tutors in mathematical logic and other topics. This was all my own anachro-feminist initiative. However, my education served chiefly to enlarge my feelings of grievance, for our library was riven with gaps and lacunae. It was actually only nine hundred books, and even though we housed them on the top floor with titanic barrels of dehumidifier salts, they were continuously succumbing to disintegration. Therefore I shouted in frustration, "But what is a Hittite!?" and "What is a kipper!?" and "They used to have illuminated books!" I could never achieve a comprehensive knowledge.

By noon I was fatigued. Sometimes I tried to refresh myself with fizzy camel milk and fruit, and sometimes I went unconscious for an hour, but it mattered little because after that I had nothing to do. I was trapped like a scorpion in a jar. This was the time of day when I usually succumbed to a staring madness. I would tell myself I should take a walk, but then I couldn't decide what shoes and clothes to wear. I would tell myself to continue reading, but I could not make the words resolve into ideas. My thoughts scattered like marbles. Sometimes I just sat naked on the floor with one boot on. Sometimes I drank poppy juice to console myself. I had no true public existence. I had no trajectory except as a wife and mother, although I secretly kept my womb untenanted by eating a monthly abortion medicine that my father's clown Edward Halloween bought from a slave magician. This medicine was exceptionally illegal, but I didn't care. It was another small exercise of my anachro-feminist prerogative.

At night we would have date wine in the garden, which was nice, but then we had state dinners with hereditary senators or visiting dignitaries from the MDC. These dinners were an agony of repeated courtesies, although they were much better than my nights with Anthony Fucking Corvette. He was a coarse frolicker who didn't give a good damn about anything. He ate sorghum paste and peanut soup, he drank muddy water, he drowned his faculties in wine, and then he heaved himself on top of me. Our wedding was scheduled for December, which was a traditional time. Daniel Defoe had come to us in late summer.

Originally, the only thing that remodernization changed was that Edward Halloween found himself less occupied. In former days he had been ceaselessly busy with his job of singing, dancing, telling jokes, and playing the flute at orgies, but now my father decided that consorting with clowns was an indulgence unbefitting a serious monarch and president. He spent all his time with Daniel Defoe, though you could have argued that he had only exchanged one clown for another. In any case, Edward Halloween and I were left alone more often, which was nice for me but surprising for him, for he was dismayed to see how I passed my days.

"How do you stand it?" he said. "A person must have some occupation. How do you while away sad afternoons? Just a few days of this boredom and already I want to espouse anarchy and bring down the state in a crashing fiery cataclysm."

He decreed a private clown's decree that we were no longer allowed to do nothing. Each day we had to do at least one activity. And that was how we came to make our first exploratory nighttime venture into the city. I wasn't supposed to leave our compound because there was a danger of catching dog malaria or being murdered, and previously I had only seen the poor sections of St. Louis from the window of a horsedrawn automobile, but Edward Halloween was right. Sometimes you have to throw caution to the hounds.

First we disguised ourselves. I removed my silver armlets, put on a pink cotton dress, and circled my eyes with greasepaint. He wore rough cloth pants and no shirt, like a river boy. Then we crept away through the contingency escape tunnel and walked all the way across the city to a place called Fat Tuesday's, which was next to the national lottery shack in the Tokyo neighborhood. For several hours we drank banana beer with the hookers and rat catchers and denture servants. It was an outstanding location. They served banana beer in earthenware cups, and you could pulverize the cups afterward because they were disposable. The ground was carpeted in red dust and pieces of cups. There was also a charcoal pit where they char-roasted barbeque shamo and goat, and all the tables were assembled from palm trunks split down the middle and fastened together with the flat side up. This was said to be the fad in the Mississippi jungle, for people in St. Louis had an enduring fascination with the Mississippi jungle. This is why they drank banana beer, for example, which was expensive and didn't have the smoothest finish.

Edward Halloween was mostly incognito, but my accent betrayed me and several people tried to speak to me in Modern English. They knew I was a rich person. One man grinned and said, "If you would try to have perfect shoes, okay! Good on you!" But later an angry woman shouted, "Explain it please, why are they genius scientists, but it still have no cure from a zombie bite?"

These nighttime ventures became regular with us, at least for a few weeks, and I learned more of St. Louis on those nights than in twenty-six years of high privilege. I liked to keep silent and fantasize that this was my real life. It was only noise and torchlight and wheeling stars and nothing more, no state dinners, no engagements, no stuffed-pepper atmosphere of a president's house and a president's aspirations. It was the air and savor of liberty. It was men playing dice, and they kept score by clipping clothespins to their beards, and it was a woman with arbitrary letters shaved into her hair, and it was an embalmed decorative rat stuffed with aroma berries. Sometimes there were even MDC men from across the river, where I had never been. You could identify them by the perfumed wax that they employed to shape their hair into high crests and ridges. They came to visit the brothels. There were no brothels in the MDC because, if you believed my father, their president was an enemy of private enterprise.

Edward Halloween was addicted to banana beer in addition to sweet potato wine and palm wine and date wine, and he was also addicted to millet beer. Millet beer was only for very poor people, but he relished it best of all because it smacked of his childhood, before his uncle made him a eunuch and sent him into service as a clown. Usually he was so fuckered up by the end of the night that I had to stuff his cheeks with cocaine leaves so that he would have the energy to walk home, and this was the precipitating factor in our discovery. One night he was so badly poisoned with cocaine and beer that he could not cease himself from belting out poor person songs as we returned home through the contingency tunnel. The presidential guards came hustling down and found us there. After this my father posted nighttime guards at my door.

1560

Daniel de Fo has persuaded the alcalde to organize a new expedition to the land of cinnamon. The alcalde has been preserved until this time by his own misery, as vinegar and salt preserve vegetables, but the prospect of riches excites him, and the prospect of converting the Indians excites him even more, and he grows more spirited as he begins to put the expedition together. Surely he will be admitted to heaven for this great service to God? Surely he will be able to buy a papal dispensation as well, should he still desire to commit suicide?

"It is knowing the time and seizing the opportunity that makes men prosperous," he says.

I encourage him to come with us, but he refuses. I say it will get him away from the pigpen, but he says there are pigs in the jungle as well. He is not wrong. A Pirahao pig is baaí or baahóísi. In Spanish it is called a peccary.

So the alcalde looks forward to his salvation, and Daniel de Fo looks forward to his reunion with his lost love Anna Gloria, whom he will send for when he has made himself rich, and I do not know what I look forward to. Now that I know the expedition will become a reality, my sense of grievance has become rarefied. My desire for vengeance has become a story I tell myself.

For now there is nothing to do. We sit by the crashing muddy sea and chew pieces of sugarcane, which the Christians have just begun to plant. We eat coconut candy. We eat the eternal cashew fruits and peanuts and guavas. We look forward to a time when the world will be a different place, and we ourselves different in it, and this is the Christian way of living.

The alcalde arranges for the ships that will take us west to Panama, the first leg of our journey, and he writes letters to the officials there. He hires a pirate named Gonzalo de Castellana to captain the enterprise because Daniel de Fo has insisted that he is too old to command troops himself. He recruits soldiers and sailors from elsewhere in New Granada and from the islands as well. Some of these men expect to make their fortunes on the expedition, but most of them are poor and their greatest ambitions fit into an oilskin bag. They hope for a handful of golden ornaments that they can exchange for a piece of land, a few sheep, fewer cows. One man tells me that his only desire is to own a pair of French shoes.

Some of these men have the yellow faces of men persecuted by God. Some of them worry that they have the devil inside them. One man tells me that the devil showed him a book written in blood and explained that he had only to sign his name and he would never again have to labor as he had always done. The devil would chop his firewood for him. The devil would help him make a house with plaster walls. He has not signed the devil's book, but if the expedition is a failure he will have no choice.

Some of these men are persecuted by other Christians because of the way they choose to worship God. Some like Daniel de Fo are conversos, exiled from Spain and doomed to wander the earth. I am like a converso also. When I speak Spanish I feel that I know God, but when I'm asleep God is only a monkey with the face of a young woman. He is a Pirahao man with no teeth and he has stolen the keys to the sky. He has a son named Hiso. He has no power over the things of the forest.

We meet a Christian heretic named Miguel Oreja. He too has been exiled from Spain, though he has never been a Jew. He is a large and impressive man with a head like a cube of limestone. He cares nothing for riches. All he wants is to convert the Indians. He is well-liked and well-respected, but he is an unstable character and sometimes he vanishes into a world of gods and ghosts. He tells us that it is a sin to cross the street because crossing the street is so uncompromising an expression of individual will that it constitutes an affront to God. At the same time he believes that man is capable of perfection. He says that man is capable of looking upon God and contemplating his glory in this life and not only in the life to come.

"This appeals to me," says Daniel de Fo. "I've started to worry that my days in this world are going to be innumerable."

Daniel de Fo says that he visits Anaquitos in his sleep. Sometimes, high above the vast plazas, he sees a hanging swinging basket suspended beneath a wineskin full of hot air. I don't remember this floating wineskin. Sometimes he sees enormous men in sleeveless doublets and short baggy hose. They play a game with a rubber ball. They run and jump and toss the ball through a loop of iron high up on the wall. I cannot remember this game either. Sometimes he sees Anaquitos as it will be many years in the future. It is a devastated city at the edge of a desert. There are camels in the streets. There is a Christian king named Roletto, and he has a daughter named Yasmina, and the people are starving.

I also visit the city when I'm asleep, but I always return to the same house and I always say the same things. I try to apologize but I can only apologize in Spanish, and no one understands me.

On other nights I visit different cities. Sometimes, because I have become sick with the Christian disease of looking into the future, I visit cities that don't exist yet. They are grey and endless and they glow with lights of all colors. They are bright and dark all at once. The noise is unbearable. The people have forgotten how to see. The only animals are purple doves.

I have more and more trouble moving between night and day. I have more and more trouble deciding what I am and what I want. Sometimes I don't know if I'm speaking Pirahao or Spanish.

We tell the soldiers stories about Anaquitos, which we call El Dorado. Daniel de Fo says that in El Dorado they will be able to eat as much rat meat as they like. They will be able to wear clothing dyed every color imaginable and some colors that cannot be imagined. They will be able to go to the zoo and see the karawa bird, which is ten feet tall and appreciative of fine singing. They will be able to dance with the big bird and sing the tapir song.

I tell them stories too, but only because this is what I have always done. I have no reason for saying what I say. I tell them that in El Dorado the people bury their dead idolatrously, with many golden objects and with dead animals too, so that the dead person will have food in the life to come. I say that they always void themselves in full view of their children, so that the children will have no illusions about life. I say that they make sacrifices to the mountain peaks. I say that their most important ceremony is the ceremony of a boy's first haircut. I say that the men have to bind their balls up with snakeskin and rub them with a special ointment or else they hang down to their knees and eventually fall off. Daniel de Fo nods and laughs, haha.

"This trouble with balls is an effect of the heat," he says. "It comes from living under the climate of Venus and not under the climate of the moon."

The river was falling farther every month and our grain reserves dwindled away. I was not starving, nor famishing for want of water, nor forced to live on poppy juice, which stopped you up back and front, and this minimum comfort was all a person could ask for in such times. These months burned away one after another and time brought only increased suffering. The river lands were stressed by salt, and farther inland the banana trees were all dead, and the millet was tiny, and the sorghum became poisonous. Then November came again, and again the skies were clear and bright. It had transitioned from a familiar periodic routine drought to an emergency of agricultural famine, and the city was rife with periodical grain riots, long water queues, and righteous fury. My father had to increase the guards around the strategic dikes and waterworks. His singular fear was that a well-regulated militia would rise up and break the social contract.

"What thrives in a drought?" said Edward Halloween. "Poppies, mama beans, and revolution."

Since we were forbidden from leaving the palace, the calamity was mostly just a distant murmur on the dry wind. In the mornings, when I slipped out to the roof with my hot caffeine, all I could truly see of it was a featureless blue sky without depth or blemish. There should have been mist and rain and roistering clouds, but there was only a feverish sun, which at its low declension cast all the world in deep golden sunset shadows, and the enigma was that it was very beautiful, even though it was the drought, even though it was the end of the world.

My father said the answer was more intensive farming, and he decreed that no land could lie fallow, not even steep hillsides. But how could a more intensive agricultural scheme produce a plenteous crop if we didn't have enough water for the previous level of agriculture? Then he instituted a variety of strategically repressive measures. He arrogated to the government the whole sum of our meager harvest and placed the city on a ration system, as he had already done with sesame oil. He preached austerity in food consumption. He required brigades of children to haul water from the river in buckets. But he also decreed that citizens had to smelt iron in their yards and deliver a certain quota each month, and no one could grasp his intention in this. Then he decreed that it was unlawful to speak of his decrees. All of these decrees were enforced with coercive violence.

One day he was illuminated by the sunlight of genius, or so he said, and gathered us all together, including the servants and slaves and vice-secretaries, to announce an original scheme for irrigating the unirrigible lands far from the river. We would use an infrastructure of rubber hoses! He passed around an ancient piece of paper which showed a man spraying water from a coiled tube. This picture was profoundly melancholic, for it depicted a vanished world of consumer choice. The words "XHose Pro Expandable" were legible in fading red ink, but only a low percentage of the gathered crowd knew how to read.

President Roulette stood up on his throne and shouted that we would create hoses that were ten miles long. We would connect them to wind pumps and run them to the arid desiccated devastated farmlands, and our country would once again be fruitful and teem with corn and cassava and even bananas. We would grow the rubber ourselves, in the south, and sell the excess to the MDC.

Now he called upon Daniel Defoe to help him decide where the rubber plantations should go. Together they scrutinized some maps and charts. Then Daniel Defoe said, "Here's the city of El Dorado. Was it always in Arkansas?"

"If the map says so, then that's the truth," said my father.

"I didn't remember it was in Arkansas. I thought it was up the Orinoco. He said that was the place where rubber originated, so that was the proper place for our own trees. It was also good because El Dorado was on the Delta Bay, so the rubber could be floated to the river and then poled all the way up to St. Louis. The only problem was that these lands were said to have reverted to barbarity, but my father had a solution for that. He would decree a special type of colony, which would be called the Extractive Rubber State of El Dorado. He would send an expedition down the river to forcibly nationalize some cropland, and when the trees were planted he would have guards enforce Reunited States law exclusively within the rubber groves.

We all knew that this scheme would produce no rubber at all for many years, and probably never, so it would not answer to the current climate of disaster and famine. Even my father knew this, although he simultaneously didn't know it, because even he could not gainsay his own decisions. Therefore we all stood silent as cockroaches in the vast echoing chamber. The only sound was the sound of Christopher Smart licking himself.

Then Edward Halloween decided to exercise his clownish prerogative of speaking truth to power, like the clowns of ancient drama who alone of all the characters were allowed to utter true statements. From the back of the room, he shouted, "No! Listen! It is like peeing in your water jar instead of peeing all over the place! You have to understand that it's peeing either way!"

No one had ever challenged my father in this way, and now even Christopher Smart was silent, watching and waiting. But my father was inflated with the winds of optimism, and he pressed forward without acknowledging the disruption. He said that it was almost as if the rubber trees, which would be grown from seeds, would themselves function as the seeds of a new economic prosperity. Sovereignty would simply spread outward from the Extractive State and into the surrounding lawless Mississippi jungle territory.

Now we were all dismissed, but Edward Halloween had been galvanized into an unexpected rage. I cannot say why this had angered him so much. It was just one straw too many, perhaps. He rushed to and fro on the outside patio, kicking up the aromatic dust and shouting. He was an outraged figure under the arching high empty pallor of the blue sky. Daniel Defoe and I attempted to pacify him with words and affection, but it was to no avail. I had to mix poppy juice into his wine to mute his treasonous ravings.

"They cut my balls off and dress me in costumes and force me to give silent ear to these idiocies!" he shouted. "My life goes sour like fermenting mangoes. You are all I have, dearest princess Jasmine." And then he pointed at Daniel Defoe with two quivering fingers. "But you! You prop him up in his king's madness. You play into his hands. You advise him! No more. Now is the time for anarchic feminism and sectarian violence. Now we give him no quarter."

"Please drink your poppy juice," I said. "You have to stop talking or they'll pull your guts out by your tongue."

Daniel Defoe agreed with me. He tried to divert our clown's mind with stories. "I will tell you the natural history of mermaids," he said.

"No stories!" shouted Edward Halloween.

Then Daniel Defoe appeared to meditate upon a new strategy. I felt a pang of love for him, and then a concurrent pang of loneliness, and then a pall of ennui.

"You are right to be outraged," he said quietly. "We are prisoners here."

"And what I'm declaring now," said Edward Halloween, "is we should do something about it!"

"Ah, but look around. Time will take care of it for you. There is nothing so ephemeral as a kingdom. But meanwhile you do have to stop talking or they will pull your guts out, like our princess says."

DANIEL DEFOE WAS CORRECT THAT TIME WAS taking care of the Reunited States. My father sent a delegation down the river to set up plantations in the Extractive State, for example, but they never achieved their goal. The whole bedraggled cohort came crawling back one day soon afterward. It was the hour of the piggybank, when petitioners came to beg my father for alms or discourse to him on investment opportunities, and the audience room was thronged with hungry dusty people. When my father saw his delegation, he had a seizure of generosity and tossed copper dollars into the crowd, but then the people began rioting amongst themselves and had to be violently subdued by the presidential guard. Then the room was cleared.

A vice-secretary named Green strode forward in the sudden quiet. This room had stained glass and a purple rug dyed with poisonous berries, and the throne was on a raised platform. Green looked all alone out there upon his private acre of poisoned rug, but he manifested a great courage. He said there was unrest and even revolt in the southern countryside.

"They held us prisoner for a little while in Camel Flats," said Green, "where they have elected themselves an interim revolutionary president. They say this is a federation without representation. They let us go so we could come give you the message."

My father required a few moments to understand what Green was telling him.

"They elected their own president?"

"Her name is Rosa de Piedad. We didn't meet her."

"That's the most undemocratic thing I ever heard. How are we supposed to remodernize this place? Are they angry about the smelting?"

Green answered him with grave unsmiling courtesy. "They're hungry."

"It's because of this pattern of disobedience that I've had to institute austerity policies in the first place."

But I could not stand to listen to any more of this. I departed the audience room and went out into the parched garden.

Here in the quiet afternoon, I felt like an occupant of someone else's dream. I joked ruefully with myself that my father should be pleased, for inevitable collapse was the destiny of his revered United States as well. They had succumbed to factional disputes about the extension of slavery into the western territories, including Missouri, and they had succumbed to demographic wizening and the explosion of population, and they had eaten too much candy corn and poisoned the sky. They had even succumbed to droughts, as we were succumbing now.

But I no longer cared about the fall of the United States. Nor did I specially lament the passing of the Reunited States either. Instead I felt mournful that my own life would be reduced into historical footnotes, just as had happened with all the once singular figures of the past. This was the sorrow of history books, which obliterated the details of life and told only the details of politics and war. I had a wish that every history were a sentimental history as Daniel Defoe was wont to compose, for it was the sentimental and poetic truth that I longed to know. What did snow smell like? Did gorillas have fingernails? When you lifted from the earth in a spaceship or aeroplane, was it like standing up too fast? Who made my plastic boots? Was it a woman who, like me, felt hemmed in by her milieu, and ate abortion medicine to keep herself free?

I could never know these things. The only glimpse I had of a true past was the glimpse I had in the fictions of Daniel Defoe. All the uncounted myriads of other histories, the true fictive histories of all those vanished people, were lost forever. And also, in any case, Daniel Defoe would leave someday and carry on with his true life, and then I would have nothing at all. Time would stretch out in the sunlight of the ages like Christopher Smart on the ballroom floor, and when the historians of posterior days came to write the history of our time, it would be the same as every other history book. It would be the history of my father's remodernization action committee, his reforms, his unilateral legislative changes. No one would know that for me the sentimental truth was a hard blue window high up on the wall, and date wine, and mornings on the roof under that incommensurate sky and laughter with Edward Halloween, and an ache and pit of longing for Daniel Defoe, who loved another, and after and above it all, like music from another room, the feeling of life passing by.

1560

We descend through the clouds and into the forest, where there are mushrooms as big as houses, more monkeys than leaves, no up and no down and no heaven or hell. Instead of trees there is only one tree, as large as the world, with innumerable trunks, with leaves and fruits of every possible variety. The forest does not exist in Spanish, language of cows and wheat and war. It does not exist in Pirahao, language of city streets. Only the Muro can see the forest because only the Muro have words for it, and suddenly our Muro guards are much more considerable than they were at the start. They walk one in front of the other, making no sound, their hands crossed on their chests. They show us what roots to eat. They hunt and fish. Their reasons for helping us are their own. They could escape very easily. They burn their hair into a rounded fringe.

Daniel de Fo speaks to the Muro and together they decide our route. The rest of us are lost. In this state of helplessness a surprising thing happens. Miguel Oreja, who has taken charge of the expedition by universal acclamation and by the bloody suppression of alternative claimants, grows mild and cheerful.

He claims to perceive in all of this the hand of a benevolent God. He makes speeches in which he says that in El Dorado we will found a new church, free of the corruptions of the apostle Paul. He says that God will be served and honored there more than in any other place on earth. He rejoices to think that we are the agents by whom God is pleased to bring the Indians to an understanding of the Faith.

"Truly they must be a godly people," he says, "if they are anything like our beautiful Maria."

We will not conquer the city at all, he says, shaking his fists in the underwater gloom of the forest. Instead we will simply reduce it to civility by introducing private property, wages, horses, industry, the use of money, and Spanish goods. We will teach the people to wear shoes, to speak as we speak, to cook meat in the right way, to walk properly, to cut their hair.

"Indians in a state of nature are just like children," he says, "easy to persuade, and under the influence of a hot and humid temperament that inhibits them from making rational choices and exercising free will."

Everything he says is wrong, and everything he says is the truth, and I can't tell the difference in any language, but now I understand something about the difference between the Christians and the Pirahao. It is true that none of us can see the forest, but for me it is a void and for the Christians it is populated by the familiar ghosts and devils they carry with them wherever they go. This is why the Christians can cross the ocean so easily. This is why they can live in cities and in the forest and in the mountains. This is why they never flicker in and out of existence, as I do. Christianity is the world of things that don't exist, and nothing can harm it, and nothing can intrude upon it, and it is everywhere all the time, and they are always at home in it. That is how I come to understand that I am not a Christian, and never have been. After I realize this, I begin to exist again, if only a small amount.

This is also why they can disagree so profoundly among themselves. Each of them lives in a world apart, and each has his own relationship to the ghosts and spirits and gods. Now we have an illustration of this, because not all of them agree with Miguel Oreja. There is a one-eyed man named Avellaneda who says that the violence with which we've been living on our expedition, and all the violence of the religious wars in Europe, and the destruction of Tenochtitlan and Tahuantinsuyu, is in truth the violence of Armageddon. If we can look forward to a period of harmony in El Dorado, it's only because our arrival there will be marked by the return of no less a person than Jesus himself. He will rejoice at the conversion of the Indians, he will reign in love for a thousand years, but at the same time he will ring in the horror and majesty of judgment day. At this time the great majority of us will be damned forever.

"Do you think it's strange," says Daniel de Fo, "that a thousand years does not seem so long to me? To me it's like saying 'all afternoon' or 'a whole week.'"

These theological differences are irreconcilable, but at least there is no more violence. Avellaneda and a few other men simply depart one morning with cordial wishes for our happiness and success. Avellaneda makes the argument that because no one knows where El Dorado is, it cannot be said that in striking off on his own and travelling in an entirely different direction, he is not also, as surely as we are, going to El Dorado.

Daniel de Fo and I stay with Oreja because the Muro stay with Oreja and they are our only hope of remaining alive. We do whatever they tell us. When the Muro say that August is the month for ridding oneself of parasites, we eat the leaves they gather and in the morning we eliminate a menagerie of diverse creatures. We feel stronger afterward. And this is also how I learn that Daniel de Fo is a Jew after all. If he were a Christian, he could not take the cure, because for the Christians

Indian medicine is a terrible poison that sends them directly to hell.

"But what is a Jew?" I ask him. "In what world do the Jews live?"

"Good questions," he says, but he doesn't answer them.

Soon Oreja has gone mad, as every captain general must, but it is the madness of love. He gives speeches each night on the subject of the Indians of El Dorado. He says that God has told him everything. He says the Indians already have a rudimentary knowledge of Christianity. He says they know that God has given us a heaven and a day of rest. He says that even though they worship the lightning, there is no witchcraft. He says there is no evil of any kind in El Dorado.

"And there are no whores!" he says. The men look disappointed, but Oreja is beaming. "The women are not given liquor and they are always pure until marriage! Isn't it true, Maria?"

"It's true," I say. And it may be. El Dorado is a Christian city that I have never visited.

He asks me to share some Indian prayers. I invent one that will please him. "O Lord," I say, "where are you? In the sky? On earth? In the inferno? Where are you?"

"This prayer demonstrates an aspiration to be Christian," he says.

This is the central problem for the Christians in America. If God is infinitely powerful, then how could there be so many people with no knowledge of him? Oreja imagines that they have simply lost this knowledge in the long journey from Jerusalem to the New World. But it is a problem that bothers him more and more as we travel deeper into the forest, because now we begin to see wild Indians. They are naked bewildered people. They speak languages that neither I nor the Muro have ever heard. They make their arrows in an unfamiliar way and they are as far from a knowledge of Christianity as a rock is from singing the tapir song. The Muro say we must leave them alone. This is not the season for making friends. But Oreja feels he must comply with the letter of Spanish law and make an attempt to bring these people into the faith, so he orders the reading of the Requerimiento. This is a Christian story that describes the origins of the world, the nature of the Spanish monarchy, the existence of God, the existence of his representative on earth, who is called the Pope, and all manner of other things. Its purpose, says Daniel de Fo, is to establish a legal basis for conquest.

"It works like this," he says. "We claim the lands and territories for the monarchy, which makes the Indians Spanish subjects. Then, if they refuse to convert, they're said to be in rebellion and they can be attacked. This is just simple jurisprudence and legal maneuvering. Of course it's not the same thing as justice."

The royal notary is gone, so Daniel de Fo reads the Requerimiento himself. He reads it in Spanish. It must be read in Spanish because only in Spanish do these things exist. He reads the story each time we see wild Indians, and they do not understand what he tells them. Then Oreja decides that I should translate the story into Pirahao. Some of the men believe this is a heresy because it suggests that God does not have the power to make the story comprehensible to the Indians regardless of the language in which it's read. Oreja argues that I myself am the agent through whom God will make it comprehensible. It doesn't matter because it is not possible to speak a translation, nor do the Indians understand Pirahao. In place of a translation, I tell stories of my own.

"I am the mother of bees," I say. "I am the mother of bats. Look at my army of dead men. They have stomachs in their heads and brains in their bellies."

Daniel de Fo is the only one who understands what I'm saying. He thinks it is a fair translation. Oreja asks the Muro to translate it into their own language as well, but they refuse.

We make slow progress through the forest. The mosquitoes don't bite me because I only exist for a few moments at a time. They don't bite Daniel de Fo because his blood is thin and sour, like vinegar. They bite the Christians and the Christians speak of heaven, in which there are no mosquitoes. Meanwhile the Muro hunt and fish. They find roots. They milk the trees. The mosquitos bite them but they don't care. September is the month in which it is proper to die, but we try to stay alive.

I have forgotten my desire for vengeance. Now I understand that it doesn't matter whether Anaquitos is destroyed or not, because as soon as the Christians arrive it will be known to their gods and it will become a Christian city. It will become El Dorado. What can be done? The Christians are only the groping fingers of their gods.

Oreja laughs and raves and pulls at his hair. He is dissatisfied with the Requerimiento and offers explanatory appendices. He asks me to explain how wonderful everything will be in El Dorado. It will be a place of concord and harmony. There will be bread every day, and wine, and meat. He pauses after each wild sentence so that I can translate. He does not understand that Pirahao means nothing to these people.

"October is the season in which it is evil to sleep under the moon," I say. "The white men are ghosts. Daniel de Fo is looking for his wife. Who will help him?"

We reach the confluence of two enormous rivers and camp there for a month in order to build a small flotilla of brigantines. Now we will travel by boat. The Muro say they will have to leave us because for them it is not the season for traveling on the water. They tell us to continue down the river until we reach a place where there are high cliffs, flattened on top by the feathered forehead of their own god, Xagigai, to whom they now address the prayer of homecoming. They say we will reach the city in twenty days. Oreja tries to compel them to stay but they slip their chains and vanish into the forest.

We eat sweet potatoes that we find in abandoned Indian villages. Daniel de Fo and I eat the white worms that live in palm stumps in the gardens, but the Christians don't know how to eat them.

We know the city is nearby because the villages are closer and closer together. There are wide clearings. There are large rounded buildings with thatched roofs like those I remember from my childhood. We know the city is close because we see people wearing the simple clothing of the Pirahao, a strip of cotton cloth hanging from the waist and no ornament but a necklace of palm nuts. These people are not Pirahao but they live within the dominion of the city.

Suddenly I recognize a hill, a bend in the river, a rock. Suddenly I am not able to speak. It is not a failure of language but a failure of the spirit. I have brought the Christians to this place, which is the only place, the last place, and it vanishes before us like corn before a knife. Daniel de Fo must translate the Requerimiento for me, which he does in the same spirit.

"I am coming home from death," he says. He speaks Pirahao very well, though I am supposed to be the only translator. "I am just appearing around the bend. Come with us. You will enjoy a bigness of honey in the rivers of the sky."

And at last we receive an answer. An old man in a canoe tells us, "I do not remember how to eat honey."

And Daniel de Fo says, "Hello, little father."

And these two old men have a conversation. They discuss fish and rain. The Indian does not fear us. He is a Pirahao and has never had to fear anything. He tells us that a terrible thing has happened in the city and then he laughs. I laugh also. A laugh that emerges from the empty air of the river.

THE CITY IS A SHORT DISTANCE DOWNRIVER and we know now that we will reach it within three days. Oreja stands in the bow with a beatific smile. He proclaims his love for all the people we see. Daniel de Fo translates.

"Where is Anna Gloria?" he says. "In the sky? On earth? In the world beneath the world?" He shouts at everyone we see. "She is a pretty woman. She has hair like the Xagai river."

When we arrive in Anaquitos, we do not find houses roofed in gold. We do not find bread made from crushed pearls. We do not find a king who covers himself in gold dust and takes a ceremonial bath each morning. We do not find white Indians. We do not find Indians with some intimation of Christian theology. We do not find the city I remember.

We abandon our brigantines on the beach upriver and walk down the white highway. We meet no resistance. There are no gates. We see the great earthen mounds, which were once as smooth as a bald man's head, and they are dotted with trees. We see the canals and streams that watered the manioc fields, and others that carried away the sewage, and they are not flowing at all. The fish ponds are dry. In the dazzling white plazas the macha trees have died and the fig trees have gone wild and pulled up the paving stones. The air is thick with flies. There are filthy people drunk at midday but many of the streets are empty and many of the houses are falling down. The market women have nothing to sell. They regard us with revulsion but without fear.

I see all of this, a city in decay, but the Pirahao do not, because for the Pirahao it is not proper to compare what exists now to what existed at an earlier time. The Christians do not see it either because they are not here, because for them Anaquitos does not exist at all. The Christians see a beautiful white city instead. They see El Dorado. They see heaven on earth.

"It's like a dream from the tale of Amadis," says Miguel Oreja.

Here is the city where I was born. I do not think about it. I can't stop thinking about it. The city will not be destroyed and it will be destroyed and it has already been destroyed, and I have no home in the world.

We march into the city and nothing happens. We stand in the white plaza looking around and waiting. The air is the color of inaga fruit. There are iguanas here and I wonder if the people have forgotten how to eat them, or if there are now so few people that those who remain cannot eat the iguanas faster than they hatch. For a long time no one speaks to us, and then a madman comes. His speech is unintelligible and his hair is matted with monkey blood. The Christians think he is a priest. I tell them there are no priests in Anaquitos. There are no rituals. There are no gods. I try to make them understand how this world is different from their world, but I know that for them there is only one world.

Here is the city where I was born, and here are the people with whom I once belonged, but I have forgotten how to see them. I can see parts of them but I can't see them whole. An old woman is a strip of cotton cloth and a yellow incisor. A hungry boy is an eyebrow and a shoulder blade. I do not think of my childhood, although I think of it continually. I do not think of the pet monkey in the basket and the tapir stew and the pieces of old pottery I dug up in the courtyard. I do not think of my father or of the days he spent teaching me to make black earth for the garden. I do not think of these things because it is not proper to think of the deep past. The deep past is not here anymore. The person to whom those things happened was called Xiako and she is not here anymore. I am Maria. I am not a Pirahao and I am not a Christian. I am nothing. I don't think of this and I think of nothing else and I am stupid like the monkey when we made him drunk with rotting fruit.

There is no time for these things. There is no time to see the city or to wonder at its disintegration, because now we must undertake the business of politics. We must convert the Indians. We must read the Requerimiento. Miguel Oreja bounces on his toes and sings. His beard is a long bawdy sailor's song.

I try to explain that there is no government to usurp, no king to negotiate with, no judges or mayors with whom we must come to terms. This city does not function in the way Christian cities function, and now it seems it does not function at all. But the Christians cannot understand this and because they cannot understand this I take them to see the Xipaohoani. These are the oldest men in each family and they meet in the house of darkness at every change of the moon, but they have no power. They make suggestions and they are ignored. They are just old men. I take the Christians to see them because there is no one else for them to see.

Miguel Oreja is very pleased. He tells me that the Xipaohoani are the city's governing body. He feels certain that once I explain the precepts of Christianity to them, we will immediately and spontaneously create a new Christian polity, the Kingdom of El Dorado, in which we will all live as brothers and sisters in Christ.

So I explain Christianity. I say, "In the upper sky there is a man. He makes the world. He has a wife but no man has eaten her. She is called Maria. He nails his son to a tree. This happens so long ago it is forgotten."

"Maria," says one of the old men. He tilts his head in my direction. I have already introduced myself as Maria. They think I am telling a story about myself.

"Yes," I say.

To himself he says, "She is Maria. Her husband makes the world."

All of this is meaningless. It is a joke. In Pirahao, a story is true only as long as someone in the story is still alive. Afterward, when there are no witnesses left, the story is never told again. A golden crucifix is an idol that represents the execution of a god in a time beyond memory. How can the Pirahao understand this? Even if they could understand it, it would be improper. Only the Christians make idols. To the Pirahao it is meaningless to revere an object.

But the Xipaohoani do not laugh, as I expect them to. They don't laugh because they know the Christians are a people to be feared, strange and disgusting as they are. And this is when I learn what happened to the city. The old men tell me that when the starving and wounded Christians came here for the first time, their presence coincided with the eruption of a plague. The Pirahao physicians, who can cure everything, could not cure it, and it was this plague that reduced the city to its present condition. Now the Pirahao have come to understand that the Christians are themselves the plague. I ask what they will do about it but they don't understand my question. There is nothing to do. I ask them if they think the plague will come again. The plague is already here, they say, pointing to the Christians.

For the Pirahao, the only truth is what happens. For the Christians, the truth is what doesn't happen, the truth is everywhere, the truth is unknowable. I know that there can be no understanding between them, but there is no way to say this that is true in both languages.

I leave Miguel Oreja with the old men, to whom he tries to speak Spanish. I walk through the city looking for Daniel de Fo. I see the houses arranged neatly around each circular plaza, but their roofs are falling in. I tell myself I am Maria. I am not Xiako. Xiako is not here anymore and her anguish doesn't exist.

Daniel de Fo is buying xaxa from a woman in the market. Rat meat and manioc. He takes a few bites and pronounces it the best thing he has ever eaten.

"If I live a thousand years, I'll never have a meal so good," he says.

He doesn't finish it. He is in the sun but he isn't sweating.

"There's no treasure. I realize this now, but you must have known it all along. You tricked me!"

"Everything was different. I apologize."

"I forgive you. But how will I get back to Spain now? How will I find Anna Gloria?"

"You have to find the world in which she exists. The language in which her name can be spoken. Otherwise you won't know her even if you're looking right at her."

"That isn't very helpful," he says. Then he laughs and shakes his head. "What if she's left Spain by now? She could be in Zanzibar, or Achem, or Goa. Every night I dream of camels and dust. What does it mean? It is the city of Aden?"

When the sun sets, there is a dance in the central plaza. I wonder if the Pirahao will murder the Christians as a way of controlling the spread of the disease, but they do nothing. They dance. They are a bare leg, a necklace of palm nuts, a wrinkled breast, a strong jaw. There are prostitutes and they are nothing but their painted black teeth. At first the Christians will not dance because they say the music is idolatrous, but then they make themselves drunk with cashew wine. The Pirahao value drunkenness but I have trouble understanding why.

Soon everyone is drunk and laughing. There is a feast. There are electric eels, brazil nuts, piranha, otter, caiman, paási fruit. I eat baahóísi, the wild pig of the forest, and think of the alcalde of Santa Ines. There is nothing funny in the world but I'm the only one who isn't laughing. I am the only one who can find no truth in any of this. The Christians are laughing and singing and Miguel Oreja is praising God and shoveling xaxa into his mouth. He is living in the kingdom of heaven and it is as good as he thought it would be. Even Daniel de Fo is happy, already thinking of Zanzibar, already looking forward to his reunion in the East Indies.

And this is how it is for weeks, laughter and cashew wine, xaxa and dancing. Miguel Oreja grows too fat to wear his armor.

The vicar general is given a medicine that makes his arm grow back. This is the conquest, which succeeds and fails at the same time, and leaves everyone babbling absurdities, their lips greasy, their cheeks stuffed with rat meat.

All I see is a doomed people, black teeth, a strip of cotton, the forest picking apart the houses at the edge of the city. The truth is what happens. The world is only what it is. The world is filling up with numbers and gods, and soon the Pirahao won't be able to live in it anymore. That is the truth. That is what happens.

RON DE MARIS

Three White Horses

On a trip to Siam we
passed through
A nameless country.
Our guide did say

It was a little known
Land and its name even
He had forgotten.
Yet it was a heaven

Of merry people.
We asked to show us
Around. There was a steeple,
A church, a barn, plus

An old farmer who claimed
He had three white
Horses he had trained,
Lovely, such a sight

As would make your heart
Joyous. But all we saw
Was a bony old nag, part
Donkey or mule all

Covered with fleas.
How could this
Sorry animal be
Three white horses,

And why was the farmer
So happy? His existence,
As others' were
Who lived here,

Was based on the belief
That *Truth is of no importance*.

GILES HARVEY

How Can I Miss You If You Won't Go Away?

It had rained, and the cars accelerating past the bus each left a fantail of spritz in their wake. Jeff leaned his head against the window, which he realized a moment later must be filthy, and sighed. The trees that lined the highway sagged and sparkled in the fading light; only their tops were still lit. He tried identifying them, to distract himself from his rising irritation, but the bus was going too fast, and the sun was already too low, and after a moment he turned away and stared at the back of the seat in front of him. He could barely contain himself. He knew he had to do something at once.

At first, he'd thought it was simply a mistake. A girl sitting three rows ahead of him, in the opposite aisle, had taken out her laptop and begun to watch a movie. Jeff assumed that it had started on its own, before the girl had had a chance to plug in her headphones—obviously no sane person was going to watch a feature-length movie, at full volume, on a packed intercity bus. He smiled sardonically, and looked around for someone with whom to share a disapproving look. There were no takers. The white-haired lady sitting across from him (a natural ally, he would have thought) was ensconced in her Kindle; the young couple in front of her were dozing, the boy's cheek flattened against the window, the girl sprawled in the boy's lap.

By now, Jeff's smile had faded. Several minutes had passed, and still the girl had not plugged in her headphones. Distant sirens, churning helicopter propellers, a taut, menacing orchestral score were audible. Was this normal? He had not been on a bus in some time but found it hard to believe that standards could have dropped so spectacularly. He craned his neck to try and catch a glimpse of her. All he could see was a dark, glistening bun of hair (like Claire's, he thought) jutting above the seat top. It trembled faintly as the bus hit a welt in the road.

Why was no one saying anything? Like him, the girl had two seats to herself, but there were people in the seats surrounding hers whose responsibility it surely was to ask her to be quiet. He had twenty-seven papers from the undergraduate course he was TAing at Columbia ("Reformation Europe In Global Perspective") that needed to be handed back at the start of tomorrow's class, plus several chapters of *The Structural Transformation of the Public Sphere* to get through for the Habermas reading group he now regretted ever having joined. He couldn't waste another second. He had to go talk to her.

Turning back to the window, on which the translucent reflection of the woman opposite was now faintly visible, he looked again at the wall of green and brown streaking by outside. He saw what he felt reasonably confident was an elm. He'd begun to learn the names of the trees in earnest only a year ago, when Claire had first started trying to talk him into wanting a child. If he was going to be a father (though this was still an open question), he felt he should at least know the names of the trees. He'd had other memorization projects as well, back then— things he wanted to be able to tell a child about, if asked, without having to look them up: the timeline of human prehistory, the Roman emperors, the periodic table—though each of these had been quietly abandoned, at one point or another, in the mad dash of daily life. All he had left now was the trees.

A Verizon billboard loomed into view. It showed a light-skinned black man with a series of concentric circles emanating from behind his head. *SIGNAL IS STRENGTH*, Jeff read. He knew he should give Claire a call. She would be starting to worry—she got so anxious these days. He'd promised her he'd give her a call as soon as he was on the road, but he was too distracted by the girl's movie to think about anything else. If he called now, he would be curt, and leave her in a bad mood. He was doing her a favor by waiting. He had to address the situation here first.

He would give the girl one more minute, he decided—one more minute, and then he was going down there. It felt good to have made a decision, and for a moment, he was calmed. He looked out the window, squinting past the reflection of the woman opposite, which had grown clearer, more solid. A square green sign at the side of the road said, *New York 127 miles*.

"EXCUSE ME?"

"Hmm?"

"I was just wondering—you don't have a pair of headphones, do you?"

"Sorry?"

"It's just, there are quite a few people on this bus besides you…"

"And?"

"You really see nothing wrong with that? Let me put it this way. I'm trying to grade papers at the moment, but I'm finding it quite difficult, with all the noise from your computer. You wouldn't appreciate it, I imagine, if I came and sat down next to you and started reading out loud while you were trying to watch your movie. Because it's kind of similar. In fact, it's pretty much the same. I guess that what it comes down to is that this bus isn't your living room, and that when you treat it like it *is*…"

Jeff realized he was moving his lips, and looked around to make sure no one had seen him. Fifteen minutes must have passed, during which he'd found himself getting into increasingly heated arguments with the girl in his head. He'd been on the verge of getting up when it had occurred to him that she might not say yes. She might say no. She might tell him that she was perfectly within her rights. She might tell him that *he* was the one who was out of line. The whole bus would be listening, and he would get only one shot at setting her straight. He needed to be firm yet polite, non-confrontational. He shouldn't preach. No one liked to be preached to.

A hulking red SUV drew level with the bus. A boy in the backseat turned to Jeff and began making fish lips. Not wanting to seem uptight, Jeff waved. The child made no acknowledgement, and Jeff had the odd, unnerving feeling of watching some sea creature wallowing obliviously behind the glass wall of an aquarium.

He looked away. The back of the seat in front of him was covered in patterned fabric—royal blue with orangey splotches. It was used, he guessed, because patterns concealed stains better than solid colors.

The phone of the man sitting behind him started to ring— the bluesy piano riff from that Muddy Waters song he'd grown to hate on account of its ubiquity.

"Hello?" he said loudly, frustration simmering in his voice. "Yes?"

The man had already received two calls from someone with the wrong number. Jeff couldn't understand why he kept answering. It was as though he enjoyed being wound up.

"No hablo español. Yes, this is four *four*, not four eight. You're calling me about thirty times a day."

The man had an over-formal, corporate-sounding voice, not the kind you expected to hear on a bus. It made Jeff dislike him intensely.

"Call the other number. What are you still doing on the line? Hello?"

They passed a billboard for Sleepy's. *The right bed has no wrong side*. It was almost completely dark out now. The trees had grown indistinct, except in their higher regions, where light still pierced the crisscrossed branches, silhouetting them against the sky. He leaned back so that he could see the reflection of the old woman across from him in the window. Her glossy white hair fell down her back and over her shoulders, and this, together with the way she held her Kindle very close to her face, gave her a look of benign frailty. Without taking her eyes from the Kindle, she unzipped the blue fanny pack she wore around her waist and retrieved a tube of lip balm. She applied it, pressed her lips together, and pouted. Did the girl's movie not bother her? He should say something for this old woman, if nothing else— to prove to her that not all young people were as inconsiderate as the girl. Perhaps she was deaf. Jeff wondered what she was reading, and also how many men she'd slept with in her life. It wasn't difficult to tell how beautiful she must once have been. How would Claire look when she was that old?

He still hadn't called her. He knew that the longer he waited, the more annoyed she would be when he finally did call, but he couldn't face it somehow. He hated talking on the phone, especially in public places. He knew already how the conversation would play out. Claire would ask him how the conference had gone, and he, not wanting to get into details on the bus—to get into the fact that all of four people had come to hear the paper over which he'd slaved for almost a year, "Taming the Lightning: American Telegraphy as a Revolutionary Technology, 1832–60," or that one of these audience members had left less than halfway through, or that afterward, an old professor, with whom he'd considered himself quite close, had ended their brief conversation with the words, "Lovely to see you, Dan"—would tell her that everything had gone fine. To which *she*, never content with generalities, thinking, in fact, that this was one of her best traits, would press him for more information, at which point he would say, "I'll tell you all about it when I get home," a line she would take to mean that things had gone badly and that he was sulking about it, which, though more or less true, he felt like keeping to himself for the time being.

There was a sudden surge in the volume of the girl's movie: hectic, swarming violins suggested that something decisive was afoot. He sighed loudly, hoping to influence the mood of the other passengers. How could they all just sit by and let this happen?

Was each person waiting for someone else to do the responsible thing? More was at stake here than his own private irritation. It was a matter of principle. It felt suddenly as though the whole edifice of civilization rested on certain habits of courtesy: when those habits were violated, you had an obligation to defend them.

The bus crested a hill and a small valley came into view. White and red streams of light coursed past each other on either side of the road. At the horizon a thin margin of smoldering orange light was still visible.

He was going down there, and that was that. He didn't care if it was awkward. Sitting here, agonizing over what he was going to say, and how she would respond, and how he would respond to her response, was far worse. He would count down from five—no, from ten—and then he would force himself to his feet.

JEFF STAGGERED DOWN THE AISLE TO THE bathroom at the back of the bus, reaching for headrests to steady himself as he went. The bathroom door was covered in the same patterned fabric as the seats. Yanking it shut behind him and twisting the lock, he winced at the sudden stark light.

"Stupid fucking fuckity," he muttered.

He had still not spoken to the girl. Before he had reached zero there had been an abrupt lull in volume—Jeff guessed that someone sitting nearby had finally had a discreet word with her, or that the girl had simply come to her senses. Either way, he was delighted, and relieved, not to have to intervene himself. Cautiously, he'd opened his folder of student papers. He'd finished grading one and had started another ("in terms of" was misused in the first sentence) when a loud, drawn-out explosion, with lots of tinkling glass, had erupted from the girl's computer.

"Fucking stupid fucking," he went on, unzipping his fly.

Twenty more minutes had gone by, but he had finally made another resolution. It was kind of brilliant, actually. He was going to walk down there, plant himself in the free seat next to the girl, and, without saying a word, hold his book open in front of her screen and pretend to read. When she asked him what he was doing, he would say,

"Oh, sorry. Is this bothering you?"

He had not imagined past that moment, but what more would he need to say? The point would be made. In a reverie of anticipated triumph, he saw the passengers in the surrounding seats, free at last from the noise, breaking into spontaneous applause; and then, at length, as word of what he'd done spread up and down the aisle, the whole bus would join in, crowning his victory and cementing the girl's utter humiliation and defeat.

He'd just needed to use the bathroom first.

It smelled strongly of ammonia; standing over the bowl, one hand pressed against the wall, he took quick, shallow breaths through his mouth. On the wall in front of him was a two-paneled diagram instructing passengers in the correct use of the toilet. One panel showed a stick man recklessly urinating in a standing position. A red X was drawn emphatically across it. In the other panel, the stick man was shown squatting, and, as the bus lurched suddenly to one side, throwing Jeff off balance, he realized how sensible this advice was. He was grateful for the Purell dispenser.

As he unlocked the door he felt a shimmer of nerves in his stomach. Why was he so anxious? It was not as though he were about to ask the girl for her number. He imagined mock-heroically narrating the moment to Claire later that evening, and the thought of the laughs he was sure to get, as well as the respect (what he was doing was rather brave, after all), hardened his resolve. He was level with his own seat when his phone began to jitter in his pocket. It was Claire. He knew he had to answer. He sat back down and, in his sweetest voice, said,

"Hi, sug. How are you feeling?"

"Is everything okay?"

"I'm fine, everything's fine. I'm on the bus."

"Why didn't you call? I was starting to get worried."

"I'm sorry. You wouldn't *believe* what's happening?"

"What?"

"No, nothing bad." Christ: he had to watch what he said to her. "It's just—there's a girl sitting a few seats ahead of me who's watching a movie on her laptop *without headphones on*."

He was speaking very loudly, he realized. He wondered if the girl could hear him.

"Why don't you tell her to turn it off?"

"I'm going to," he said, but even as he spoke he felt his confidence leaving him; his plan was ridiculous, and a little creepy, he now saw. "It's just, I worry I've waited too long. You know, it's like a precedent's been set."

"If it's bothering you, you should tell her to turn it off."

He winced in frustration. He didn't want advice. He wanted sympathy. Through the window he saw a billboard for People's United Bank. It showed a photograph of two men in suits sitting at a table. One of the men, clearly an affable financial expert, was pointing at a document in front of them. The other man was nodding, a look of dawning recognition on his face. *Wealth grows over time*, the sign said. *Relationships do, too.*

"I *will*," he said. "I just find it hard to believe that someone else hasn't asked her already. It's like everyone's behaving as though there's nothing wrong with watching a movie, at *full volume*, on a bus."

"Just go talk to her."

"In fact, what I *really* can't believe is that *she* doesn't see anything wrong with what she's doing. Am I crazy? Tell me if I'm crazy. Because I'm really starting to wonder—"

"Excuse me? Sir?"

It was the man in the seat behind him. He was standing in the aisle, one hand planted on the headrest of the empty seat next to Jeff. Jeff placed a hand over the mouthpiece of his phone, and smiled up at him. The man was in his early forties, by the looks of it. He had an array of conventionally attractive masculine features—strong jaw, bright blue eyes, the lustrous, floppy hair of a shampoo commercial—that somehow did not add up to an attractive face. His broad arms and barrel chest were more impressive. A few seconds in his presence was long enough for Jeff to understand he had the kind of strength it would be bad to come up against.

"Are you going to be much longer?" he said in his deep voice.

"Sorry?"

"You're talking kind of loud."

"*Sorry*. I completely understand where you're coming from. It's just, my wife—"

Jeff stopped, and the man gave him a blank, weary look.

"Keep it short, okay?"

"Absolutely. Sorry again."

The man nodded and sat down heavily in his seat.

"Jeff?" said Claire.

"I've got to go."

"What was that?"

"Nothing. Just someone telling me to keep it down."

"Oh, fuck him. How did the conference go?"

"Fine."

"Yeah? What happened?"

"I'll tell you when I get home, okay? I probably shouldn't talk much longer."

She sighed, and he imagined the evening of strained petting and conciliation that awaited him.

"Okay," she said tonelessly.

"I'll text you when I'm getting on the subway, okay? Claire? Love you, sug."

She didn't answer, and he realized she'd already hung up.

～

Spanish Harlem, with its tower blocks and beauty parlors (D'glamour Hair Stylist, Cinderella Eyebrow Spa), was giving way to the gyms, boutiques, and galleries of the Upper East Side. It was not a subtle transition. Uniformed doormen lolled in marble-floored vestibules. Joggers bounced and swiveled at crosswalks, impatient to be off. Wherever you looked, buildings were encased in scaffolding.

The girl's movie had ended some time ago, shortly after the bright thicket of downtown Stamford had receded from view, but since then Jeff had made almost no progress with the student papers. Why had he not spoken to her? Why had he let her get away with it? In any case, there it was: a four-hour bus ride, wasted.

Now the skyscrapers of midtown were rearing up on either side of them. As the streets scrolled by, the Chrysler building bobbed in and out of view. Jeff stared at the girl's bun of hair and thought again how much she resembled Claire. If the two of them did have a child (*if*: he was still not resigned to it), and it turned out to be a girl, there seemed a good chance that in twenty years she would look like this.

On Thirty-Fourth Street the bus veered right. The other passengers were beginning to retrieve their bags and coats from the overhead rack. Jeff flipped through the stack of papers in his lap. Maybe he could read a couple on the subway.

As the bus eased to a stop outside the main post office building the driver came on the loudspeaker.

"Thank you for riding with Bolt Bus," he said, his voice prickly with static. "We hope you had a pleasant journey. Please make sure you have all your belongings before exiting the bus. Y'all have a good evening now."

Jeff joined the line of passengers and began inching down the aisle. The girl was still seated, stuffing something into a backpack. Seeing how oblivious she was to what she'd just put him through he felt his anger returning. As he drew level with her he surprised himself by sitting down in the empty seat to her left.

The girl turned to face him.

"Uh, hi?" she said.

What the hell was he doing?

Snub-nosed, with wide, pouty lips and pronounced dimples, her face looked nothing like Claire's. Her body-type was different, too—wide shoulders, fat arms, and enormous breasts, not what he'd pictured at all. She wore a tight black top with the words *How can I miss you if you won't go away?* printed in blue across the chest, and Jeff realized, a moment too late, that she would take his squinting decipherment of this slogan for lecherous appraisal.

"Can I help you?" she said, raising her eyebrows. They looked overplucked.

"You know," said Jeff, in a voice he barely recognized as his own, "this bus isn't your living room."

"Sorry?"

"I just..."

All of the arguments he'd been rehearsing in his mind had vanished. The girl held her backpack in front of her, as though to shield herself from him.

"Will you excuse me?" she said. "I really have to get going."

"Wait!" he said, more harshly than he'd intended. "I just think it's incredibly rude, and kind of shocking, actually, that a person would watch an entire movie on a bus, without headphones, and, well..." He was surprised by how quickly he'd recited the charges against her; he'd imagined it would take him a long time to get through everything he wanted to accuse her of. "Well, I felt I had to say something."

"Okay... Is that it?"

"Aren't you even going to say sorry?"

"If it was bothering you, you should've said something earlier. I can't read your mind."

"You shouldn't *need* to be told. It's basic courtesy. Don't watch an entire movie on a bus with the sound on. You are not the only person in the world."

"*Jesus*," she said, raising her voice. "Okay. Now will you please let me off the bus?"

Several passengers had turned to look at the scene that was developing. The man who'd been sitting behind Jeff was standing above them. Behind him was the white-haired lady; she was eyeing Jeff warily.

"Are you okay, miss?" the man said.

"It's just this guy," the girl said. "He won't let me off the bus."

"Sir, is there a problem?"

Jeff opened his mouth to speak but said nothing.

"Sir, why don't you just let the young lady off?"

The man was talking to him as though he were unhinged. Did he not understand that Jeff was the sane one here—was, in fact, the very voice of sanity? Up and down the bus people were muttering to each other; a few of them had their iPhones trained on him. He felt a panicky tingling in his chest that he remembered from childhood.

"*Sir?* Is there a problem here?"

Jeff swallowed with difficulty. Unsure what to say or do, he turned again to the girl. She looked genuinely worried now. Through the window behind her he could see the driver hoisting luggage from the storage compartment onto the sidewalk. A few passengers stood around him. One man had just claimed his bag, and, with an air of skittish anticipation, like someone newly disembarked after weeks at sea, was already walking off into the night.

GLEN POURCIAU

Getaway

Van had planned a getaway to a place where he knew no one and could be left in peace, the only drawback being that his mind would travel with him. Many times he'd told himself never to express an opinion again, and whenever possible not to speak. He carried a pen and pad, and when someone addressed him directly he'd reply by scribbling a note. In traffic he'd occasionally blurt out a curse or mutter in a way that disturbed him, memories of past muttering coming back to haunt him. He'd tell himself to shut up, without saying it out loud, because he couldn't stand the sound of his own voice. His notes at times failed to conceal his true nature, and few people could endure with patience his handwritten monologues. He saw himself as unfit for human society, and he could not recall any good he'd ever accomplished by opening his mouth to speak. Communication simply didn't work for him.

As he pretended to read the screen on his smartphone, someone approached him and leaned toward his chair in the gate area for his flight. He'd known the leaning man as a boy in the suburban neighborhood where they'd grown up, recognized him at once through the added weight and grey hair.

Excuse me, Les said, are you Van?

He wondered if he should admit being who he was, if he should reply at all, and if they would be seated near each other on the plane. He hadn't seen Les in decades and Les might invite him to dinner to share life stories. Rather than pull out his pad and write Les a note, Van shook his head.

Les stood straight up and offered a handshake, saying his first and last names. Van couldn't leave Les's hand hanging between them so he shook it. He rejected the idea of making up a name, and his voice could strike Les as familiar. He saw no one standing near Les, though his wife or other traveling companion could be in the restroom and could appear at his side and ask to be brought up to date. Van would have to sit quietly as Les explained who the man in the chair might or might not be. Les didn't glance behind him to see if a companion could be approaching, but he leaned closer than before and said that he knew who he was talking to and he didn't like being disrespected and couldn't understand it. He then walked away and sat in a chair by the wall.

The time passed slowly and Van heard Les clearing his throat and coughing several times, possibly a ploy to get Van to turn and look at him. Les could at any moment make another run at him, putting his mouth to Van's ear. Van googled Les as he waited and pictured Les googling him. He knew of several images Les could have found that proved he was lying, but Les did not bring his phone over and confront him with his own image.

Van kept his head down as they boarded the plane and did not see where Les sat, though he took a peek to make sure he wasn't nearby. He worried that his behavior at the airport might provoke retaliation that would ruin his getaway. He tried to sleep and forget during the flight, resisting his fear that Les might tap him on the shoulder from behind and insist on an explanation and an apology.

He saw nothing of Les while in the air or after landing, and he hopped in a taxi that took him straight to the beach resort he'd booked for several days. The odds were long that Les would be staying there, but he scanned the lobby and the restaurant at dinner for any sign of him and prepared himself to make a sudden exit. As far as he could tell the resort was free of Les, and he imagined himself on the beach the next day with a margarita and his Paul Bowles novel drowning out any thoughts that would have originated with him.

Before he could get out the door the next morning the phone in his room rang. He gazed at the phone, who could it be, no one knew where he was, if he picked it up he'd have to answer. After the ringing stopped he waited a moment and checked to see if the caller had left a message. There was no message, and he sat on the bed, his mind running. Les could have called the larger resorts on the beach until he found him and asked to be connected to his room. Van wished he could tell Les that if he got him talking he'd end up wishing he hadn't, but he cut off this line of thought; obsessing about Les would ruin his trip. The call could have come from someone working for the hotel, and Les had likely forgotten about him by now and could be having a rollicking time with friends.

Van dressed for breakfast and took the elevator down. When the door opened he started across the lobby and caught sight of Les rising from a chair and coming toward him. He saw no point in trying to flee or resist. Les stopped in front of him and raised his hands, his manner suggesting he'd like to have his say. Van looked into his eyes and waited. Les didn't expect Van to speak if he preferred not to, he said; he wanted a listener, someone to talk to about his failed life, and someone he'd known but wouldn't see again would be perfect. Think about it, Les said, and if Van decided it was okay they could meet here for dinner. No pressure, no need to reciprocate with an account of his life, just listening, and after dinner, he vowed, they'd go their separate ways.

Intrigued, Van watched Les walk away. If he could read a novel why couldn't he listen to another person's story? He ate his chilaquiles and adjusted himself to the proposal. Would he be tempted to speak? He could communicate with his face or gestures or give Les a slap on the back if the situation called for it. He spent the day on the beach with his novel, slowly sipping a margarita, and determined that he could meet Les without thinking how it would affect him.

He came down on the elevator at half past six and saw Les getting up from the same chair. It was a clear and calm evening and they sat at a table on the patio, Les declaring that the dinner was on him and ordering margaritas for both of them. He didn't mention Van's reticence at the airport or comment or furrow his brow when Van ordered using his pen and pad. At first he spoke generally about never knowing what he was doing or why he did things, beyond working to make enough money to pay his bills and support his family. Always he suspected himself of having selfish intentions and lacking good will toward others. He tended to mouth off to his bosses, for example, and shout at people who bothered him then rationalize that he felt a strong impulse to be honest in expressing himself, which was nonsense, since he well knew that he lied to himself and others and had never shown a serious interest in truth or justice. He'd been married twice, both times to women who suffered from addictions, one to prescription drugs and the other to alcohol. He liked to drink with both of them and up to a point he enjoyed acting crazy with them, arguing with whatever they happened to be watching on television and shouting at their so-called friends, most often when they were alone in the house and their friends could not hear them. These bouts of shouting led to them shouting at each other, and his kids, one from each marriage, grew up shouting. They'd both run off and struggled for years to stay employed, his son now locked up in prison for robbing people's houses, his daughter residing in some unrevealed location to keep him the hell away from her. He believed he'd wanted them for the dubious purpose of perpetuating himself, he said, and he regretted putting them in that position. His first ex-wife died from what he called unintentional suicide and he'd lost track of his second ex, who'd been fond of telling him that he needed to add an s to the end of his first name. Les confessed that he'd enabled his wives by behaving in much the same way they did, until they couldn't take the sight and sound of him any longer. He'd flunked out of AA, he told Van, clutching the stem of his margarita glass, and one idea that constantly haunted him was that he was the source of all his troubles. He injected the poison between himself and those he encountered, his voice a scourge that had dragged him around by the mouth and tongue throughout his life. His stupidity and misguidedness reached deeper than his conscious awareness, and the devastating truth, according to Les, was that he must have wanted to do everything he had done, and if he had it to do over he'd probably make the same mistakes again. What excuse could he offer for himself? he asked Van rhetorically as they were served their dinners. His worst enemy was himself, he continued, and he was always there, following himself around, insisting on his way, as if serving a Greater Les, an absurd phrase he'd coined and repeated to himself in self-deprecation for many years. He had never told his story, if it could be called that, to anyone, he said, and the longer he lived the more it burdened him. He had no illusion of cleansing himself by his admissions, and he hoped he wasn't leaving the impression that he sought advice or some remedy. A long silence ensued, and Les then apologized for intruding on Van's trip. Isn't this beef terrible? he said, and Van nodded.

Van's mind churned through words he could say, stirred by how much he and Les had in common. He remained silent but clasped his hands and jabbed his thumbs at his chest as he looked across the table at Les. Les eyed Van and their empty glasses and waved at the server. Van turned his glass upside down. Les ordered himself another drink.

MICHAEL PALMER

Poem Devoid of Meaning

We turn our heads away
from the three-headed lady

We avert our gaze
from the lizard-limbed one

the feathered one
in her wire cage

and Thimble Boy sipping
his smoked China tea

We exchange warm greetings
with the world's tallest man

(a friend of my father
across the distant years)

a giant named Saul
who has just days

to live and no more
An announcement is made:

the captain has abandoned ship
and only minutes remain

Somewhere I once read
that anyone can pilot a ship

through raging waters
should he demonstrate

clarity of mind
and purity of heart

I have removed my heart
and placed it on the deck

the better for all to examine it:
tell-tale signs of wear

among the valves
and significant rust

along the vena cava
traces of mercury

and a hint of cesium
in the left anterior

Fellow passengers shut tight their eyes
except for the three-headed lady

who notes, It is good, good enough
mon semblable, mon frère, sail on

Strange Now

Strange now to find ourselves
in these later, lateral days,
to lose ourselves in this slowing time
of a late, lateral light,
a slant abbreviated light
knowing that we all, each one,
once thought to become
waves beating, waves retreating,
wheeling, oval eyes of storm,
swallow-tales, atoms of thought,
as if there were such things
as if such things could be
could have been

We do know
that the cry
concerns no one at al
Someone first said this
at song's dark antipodes,
not one of my friends
in the Brazil of endless song,
not the poet of brilliant,
invisible colors,
who despairs of her work,
never ceases to mourn,
not the Cape Verdean singer
to whom I sent a kiss
across uncharted waters,

a kiss graciously acknowledged
night is such,
not

Icarus, not the cardinal
emerging in fire from the dense,
sugar-scented
privet, not a memory
of gentle hills
invented to please
or console, we borrow
a letter from dawn,
one from dusk,
one from the sun,
one from the sudden
rain, one last
from the howling of dogs
and claim
that this sudden alphabet
is ours

The Baby but One

Catherine Mary buried herself in the sand. Her brother had dug the hole just yesterday and the sea had refilled half, smoothing and rounding the depression. With her fat little arms, she swept the wettish sand onto her legs and the skirt of her bathing suit, laying her head back to be blinded by the sun.

"May I?" she said, and "No, you may not!" with no girlfriends there to hear, "but you may take two banana steps." Her father, near enough to hear, said, "Catherine Mary, you silly goose, you're talking to yourself again."

They were pals, Dad and Caff, as the five brothers and sisters called their baby but one. When no one else was around, they were content to sit together and chew the fat.

Father, as he was known to the tribe, was a chemist with a big stain on his cheek and neck from an accident or a mistake—it was impossible to say—in the lab. He wasn't handsome to start with, so the boiled skin, eraser-pink, did no harm, "plus," as people liked to say, he was already married and father of three.

"De-liver, de-letter, de-sooner, de-better," Catherine Mary was burbling from the sand pit.

"Baby girl," was her daddy's reply.

WAS SHE A BABY? SHE ASKED, AS she felt the tears running down her face, and why? Because she was opening her eyes in the sun. There was a reason for everything. Spilling sand every which way, she scrambled up, twisted and twirled, then fell flat on her face, dizzy, giddy, in love with life, as Father liked to say to Mother, when Mother stopped long enough to hear. Cooking, cleaning, slapping, scolding, praying, herding, and safeguarding five wild Indians kept Mother from her favorite activity—yakking on the phone to sister and father, and inviting people over for drinks. Mother was queen of the tribe, as she'd been queen of her motherless brother and sister, and her policeman father. Police captain, as Mother corrected Father, if within earshot. Were they a happy family? he asked himself when he was away five days out of seven at the cosmetics lab in greater New York. He had a little flat and everything he needed, but he pined for the queen and brood. That was who he was. Who was he? A family man, was the answer nine out of ten would give. But he was also a thinker and his thinking was done on his own time, because, in the nest, his quiet self was at the service, the beck and call really, of Catherine and the kids, each groomed for distinction, for Father and Mother were college graduates and 100 percent, if anyone asked, white collar. Mother preferred the word "professional." She taught first grade at a nice little primary school, a stone's throw from their church and its sister-school that her five children were, of course, sent to.

The perfection of it sometimes chilled the bones, or was it the cloud passing over the sun and turning the nearly empty, end-of-the-day beach into a scene resembling the afterlife: a gloomy desert and an angry, spit-colored drape of sea, whose vicious waves were ever verging closer to the child flopped, face-down in the damp blanket of beads. Caff lifted her head and caught Dad's eye, under his sunhat.

"What's up, doc?" said Dad, and, with that, Caff lay her laughing face on the now-sparkling sand. She could almost fall asleep with the flushed-out sun warming her golden-brown back.

They knew they had to get home. It was time, it was beyond time, it was late, and yet they couldn't move, in that delicious air bath of salt, pure oxygen, and the ribbons of heat and deadly night cold, just a sliver of it, as Mr. Sun disappeared again, and the lights went out for good.

DAD WAS ELEVEN WHEN HE LOST HIS own father to the Crash and its aftermath, and Caff eleven, when she lost her one and only Dad, Daddy, Poppa Bob. It was a quiet winter day and the sun had left town, just as all the factories had left in Dad's lifetime; went south, or overseas. Where the sun should be funneling through the upstairs east-facing windows was a sullen and fat pad of cloud. It was still dark when Caff tiptoed along the hallway to where Dad had his own single bed (a cot) in the sewing room, where they kept the Christmas lights and summer things in winter, winter things in summer, along with the trunks of old curtains, doilies, and dresses that didn't fit, but were too good to "throw."

On certain nights during his weekend furloughs he could be found in Mother's bedroom, snoring away; but most often that room, with closed—but not locked—door was silent, and he would turn up in his clubhouse, their clubhouse, where they played Chinese checkers and all the old board games (Candyland, Monopoly, Chance, Chutes and Ladders) that were stored in the closet, or, once in a blue moon, tackled a jigsaw puzzle, which they left on the floor to finish, or not. Old Maid, War, 52 Pickup they'd left behind with childhood—hers. His had been different, and shorter. Sometimes she blocked her ears as she sat on his knee and sipped from his highball glass, with or without its sweater. There were things she did not want to know. Oh, she knew them, but begged him, pretty please, to lie, and say he had a mother and father, aunts and uncles, cousins, brothers, and sisters, pals, birthday parties with candles; and was not, don't say it, an orphan living in a home for orphans, kept by the nuns and the biddies they hired to feed and burp, to sweep and tidy. She knew and didn't know, and sometimes he teased her with a single hint: the rough undershirts, and toyless, joyless Christmas with Mass and nothing else. Cornbread and cranberry for lunch, with a cardboard box of ribbon candy to share. She knew everything about it, but don't say!

The house was cold, meaning the furnace had gone out. She could hear her mother on the phone telling the tale to the oil man, who would visit by and by with his truck and rubber snake, and that dreamy, deep, and everlasting smell of oil filling up the tank.

Caff was tiptoeing, and why? Everyone was up. Mary Ann, number one, cooking the breakfast; Ann Mary, second in line, drinking coffee and laughing at a lame joke told by her brother, Francis Christopher, to his next-in-line, Patrick James, and little Peter Joseph crying, as always, over spilt milk. Wahh! Caff said to herself, clapping a hand over her mouth. And, "now I lay me down to sleep," as she pushed open, crack and creak, the door to the clubhouse, although they hadn't called it that in ages. Their games had changed. Father and daughter, now a big girl, and just as big as a house. Fatty, she couldn't stand to hear, unless it came out of his tender mouth and snaggly teeth, all yellow with cigarettes, cigars, and cigarillos.

She gathered her energy, her might, and kicked open the door with a slipper foot. At first, she didn't see him. The shades were pulled—green one and white one—and the curtains drawn, the winter drapes, rose-colored and dusty, on their pole.

And then, before she could move a muscle, she heard her name come singing up the stairs. "Catherine Mare-ree." She listened for its echo, and assessed its tone, deciding to squirt out the door and check. Sure enough, Mother was off the line and needing her baby girl (as Caff thought of herself, hugging her rich and puffy sides as she lay awake mornings before the sun came up, the alarm went off, and the houseful of fleas—as she thought of the rest of them—jumped to attention).

"Just a minnn-it," she sang from the top of the steps. "Is Daddy down there?"

"Get down here right now, and never mind about Daddy."

"I'm coming," she sang, but didn't start quite yet, stalling in indecision between the luscious squares of soggy toast overrun with butter, sugar, cinnamon, honey, maple syrup, grape jelly—her favorite, between that (with cocoa) and tickling the sides of her out-like-a-light Daddy, until his eyes opened and he blessed the day that God had given him such a child, almost a teen really, but so immature she was.

She stood there, stumped, waiting for her decision. "May I? No you may not, but you may take two baby steps and one banana step, three twirly-gigs, and a leap for the stars."

"Get your father up!" was the word from below, so Caff skipped down the steps, a heavy tread that alerted all ears to her arrival.

"Is he still asleep?" Mother said, brushing back her child's corn-silk hair, from where it liked to go, right into her eyes. "Where are your glasses? Where did you leave them? Retrace your steps and find them. Time is wasting."

So up pounded Catherine Mary to fetch her specs on the bathroom radiator, where she left them so they'd be warm but not burning hot when she slipped them on her nose and saw the day in living color.

⌒

Life without Dad was crime and punishment, dirty looks, a thousand snubs amid the crying and moaning. At night, she could hear, in the gloom, the bad dreams, the trips to the bathroom, the ticks of the clock, the on and off of the oil burner. The house filled with clutter, with nobody to straighten it out before his arrival, just in the nick of time. Mother was a wreck, a soldier, hysterical tears one minute, and raging temper the next. People were in and out of the house, carrying one-pot dishes, soup, platters of cupcakes and sheet cakes, fruit basket, dips and chips, boxes of chocolates, and booze. Mother could not turn off the waterworks, while Caff couldn't turn hers on. Why? She'd been the one to find him, and like a stone she was, stone-faced when she wasn't giddy, or laughing her head off. A new place in the family was found for her: the doghouse.

"Leave me alone," she said, followed by, "don't bother me." Everything about life was different, even a month, a year, ten years after. She was "never the same," people liked to say, people who knew the family before and after.

For Catherine Mary, the lights had gone out. "Remember when?" was a game, a routine she refused to play. There was a holy card with a picture of St. Anthony, because Dad was born on his feast day; Anthony was the one who resisted temptation, spending his lonely life in the desert, living in a cave. On the back, in beautiful script, was: Robert Francis Michael Donavan, and the two dates. A shamrock and the Irish prayer about the open road. Catherine Mary kept hers under her pillow in a sock. She used another as a bookmark, one was stuck in the mirror, and the extras stored in the pocket of her uniform, on the heart side, where the school badge was sewn. She studied this small card during the wakes, three nights in a row. They didn't want her to stand with the family, as the visitors lined up to kneel by the casket and shake the family's hands. They made her sit in the front row, right in front of it, so that, if someone asked, they could point her out as present. She often had a grin on her face, so you couldn't help but wonder if she'd gone mental. School pals turned up with their parents, and they'd plop down on the empty seat next to the girl who'd lost her father. "Sorry for your loss," they'd say, because they heard their parents say it. "It's not mine," she'd say, "Mind your own business. What's it to you?" Sometimes she made faces, and on the third wake day, when the priest came to say the rosary and the flowers were starting to reek as they faded and flopped, they sent her to the powder room and she locked herself in, falling asleep on the couch until the skeleton key was found, and the undertaker's wife woke her up and sent her home with the family. She had decorated the powder room with tissue roses, using up all the bobby pins in the dish. She'd powdered her face, and folded her hands on her chest, so that's what her mother saw, flinging herself in, as the funeral home was closing for the night, and Catherine Mary couldn't be found. Mother yanked her by the arm and slapped her hard, but Caff wouldn't open her eyes and had to be dragged out and pushed into the car that Mother would have to learn how to drive, now that there was no father. "What the hell's wrong with you?" Uncle Buddy, Mother's cousin said, from the driver's seat. "What a time to pull a stunt like this. Why don't you act your age!" "Leave her be," Mother said, reaching back with an arm and flapping her hand until Caff took it, and held it tight. What a relief, and a first, and maybe even a beginning. Maybe yes, and maybe no. You may take one umbrella step. May I?

FOR TEN YEARS THE SIGHT OF HIM: flat on the army cot like a baby in a bassinet, was her first thought every livelong day. "Good morning, Mary Sunshine," was his greeting at least half the time. Or, "Boo!" he'd yell, knocking her back in a frenzy of fright, his head popping out from under the pillow.

"You stupid, stupid, stupid-ass Daddy," she'd say, when she had the breath to say it, then jump on top of his big stomach, and he'd stroke her long back, up and down, or rock her back and forth, dumping her on the floor, then falling out himself in a bundle of sheet, blanket, and puff. "You hurt me," she'd say, even if he hadn't. "You're full of it," he'd say back. "Should I call the doctor or the hearse?" and she'd laugh, and up they'd get, kicking and stumbling and raising Cain, all of which could be heard downstairs. No one liked it.

Hand-in-hand, they'd dance down the steps, unless he had her on his back, baby elephant.

"What a way to start the day," the queen would say, but it was the weekend, and they were free on bail. "Settle down," they heard, and eventually they did, for long enough to eat and plan the day: hardware store, the dump, ice-skating rink or the playground, confession at 3, hot dogs and beans and a long night of fast before early mass and a day-long stuffing of donuts, sweet rolls, bacon and eggs, boiled dinner and meatball sandwiches, ordered and driven home from the one Italian restaurant. They did the pickup and Dad had a quick one at the bar, with time to put a quarter in the jukebox and hear "Volare" or the Mexican hat dance, or the theme from *Exodus*. Name that tune, Ed Sullivan, and good night Mrs. Calabash, wherever you are.

"Careful," was a word she heard daily, hourly. Care-full. Or, "go easy," because she was fast and rash and a buttinski. So, carefully, that morning she tiptoed in the dark toward the spot where the cot hugged the wall, arms straight out, fingers extended, loping like a ghost or sleepwalker.

At eighteen, she still had her baby fat, her face round as a pie, or a full moon. No boyfriends, although she liked to sit around and and chat up the sisters' dates. She could make them laugh, although pesty and dragging out the time spent in Mother's house, which was now tidy and clean, polished and carpet-swept, filled to the brim with knick-knacks, now that there was no one around to break them. Turning over a new leaf was what they had to do as kids grew up and "impressions" were so quickly formed and lasting.

Mary Ann was engaged to a Protestant with a lot on the ball, and Ann Mary had joined Opus Dei as a secular nun, free to live wherever she wanted, but chaste, a soldier in the pope's army. Francis Christopher, or Frankie as he called himself with his cronies, was into politics and had interned at the state house, and then worked for the Yankee senator, but not for long, as the children of ward-heelers were taking over the city from the grassroots. He had a future ahead of him, people liked to say, because he had the gift of the gab, just like his mother and grandpa, as well as the ties to and pull from the Ancient Order and Friendly Sons, not to mention the Fraternal Order. That didn't hurt, and wouldn't, in getting out the vote when he ran against a Kennedy boy whom the family had set up with a city address and a degree from the Christian Brothers' college. The guy was in like Flynn, but Frankie was no quitter, and ran once, twice, three times, before he threw in the towel, and wouldn't you know it, the Kennedy was elected to Congress, and the seat opened up again in the General Assembly. By then, of course, Frankie had other irons in the fire, although not burnt out, or on the sauce, as people said, and will say about anyone who got their name in the paper.

Patrick James joined the Jesuits, following his Uncle Mike on his mother's side—and, without the uncle, would he have gotten a foot in the door with his poor school record and iffy health (a trace of TB and rheumatic fever, which kept him a year out of school, relying on his mother's talents in the grammar school to boost him through eighth grade, with the books the nuns sent home). He'd always been a holy joe, and no clown or fly-by-night, so the Jebs got a bargain, the uncle said, and maybe told them.

Peter Joseph joined the force, and boarded in the Donavan summer cottage, fixed up for winter residence with an oil burner and storm windows. Never married, a scout master, loyal Son of St. Patrick, knight, rosary and altar, and holy name societies. Pillar of the church, the old St. Mary's Star of the Sea. Was he a drinker? Did he play the horses? Was he spotted in the combat zone of his native city, taking the air, loitering? Who's asking?

One day, when it was raining cats and dogs, Catherine Mary fell down the cellar steps and fractured her arm and wrist. She lay on the floor for who-knows-how-many hard hours, knocked out, and then unable to rise on a sprained ankle, until her mother came home and woke her up, clomping in the kitchen overhead. With just a bathrobe and slipper, Caff, chilled to the bone, called out in a raspy, phony-sounding voice the mother chose to ignore for the time being. "What are you doing down there, anyway? Get up here and help me unload the groceries."

"Did you hear me!" she yelled through the cellar door, where cans and root vegetables were piled on the stairs. The light sliced into the gloomy hole where the girl (girl! She was forty!) lay, stiff as a board but still in pain-dulling shock. It was only when her mother stuck her head in, and flipped on the cellar light, that she saw what she saw, and it was a sight to see, and almost stopped her heart.

It was his heart that had stopped was the verdict on why the Donavan father had died at fifty—not even—forty-seven he was. He'd died, they said, in his sleep, peacefully. But when? was what his youngest daughter wanted to know, and insisted on knowing, pestering the priest, the coroner, the undertaker, whomever she could buttonhole later on that day of days. Sorry for your loss is all she got.

Catherine Mary was too stout for her mother to gather up the wreck that was her baby but one, so what were they to do? They were both crying, and mother full of admonitions, accusations, and instructions, which brought on the brain fever that almost killed the girl, lady, old maid, biddy, hen, or whatever label people had to hand to slap on a situation that was no longer tolerated or seen as normal.

The rescue squad came, as they had on that day of days, and it took three of them to haul her up the rickety steps, after they stabilized the pitiful arm, twisted and crushed beneath her.

She thought she was on her way to join her daddy, or that's what she dreamed in her fever. Going where he was, in a place reserved for her, by his side, there in the clouds with the saints and martyrs and other connections in the Donavan-McCarthy family.

But no, she was sent home a week later, in the back of Paddy Jim's Buick. Caff was his favorite baby sister, or came to be when she had nothing to hold onto but him.

Instead of going straight home from the hospital, the priest drove his sister to their favorite restaurant as kids, a tea room off a back alley, across from the department store that owned it.

And there so long (chicken croquettes, lemon-meringue pie, and a few little toasts of Irish highballs) that the mother was worried sick.

Died and rose again, was what Catherine Mary kept thinking. I died and rose again, died... Sent to rot in hell, but rose again. And here I am (she was on painkillers, penicillin, and tranquilizers) at Shepard's Tearoom.

They had a good laugh, Father Pat and Sister Caff, a good laugh, and even a third tall one before the priest consulted his watch and saw he was late for confessions at the cathedral, where he was working his way up from secretary to auxiliary, a feat that would take twenty long years.

He pulled the car around, and two of the waitresses, one on each arm, helped the lame sister, dizzy and awkward on her too-tall crutches.

Her mother received her with her frantic worry lapped over by the calm of a native dignity, and a quick one. The daughter's bedroom was prepared, but not for the daughter. Mother would take the back bedroom, leaving Caff the master, and that was how it remained well beyond the girl's full recovery. She was back at her job receiving visits and calls at the insurance office, typing and taking dictation, although the wrist and hand were warped, and two of the nails mangled. Everyone asked, and the story rolled out with a dollop of wit and self-mockery. Caff was appealing in her stout matronhood, and never lacked a friend of the male persuasion, including her boss, younger, and no longer a bachelor. It was a two-man office, and Caff was sitting pretty with easy hours and long vacations. She took her old mother to see the fall foliage, and they bussed as far as Canada and back to celebrate the old lady's seventy-fifth birthday.

They came to resemble each other, and it was hard to tell which was which, as they trundled in, arm in arm, for the seven o'clock mass, seven days out of seven, and stopped at the creamery for coffee and donuts, tea and a fried egg. Sometimes the cook had to switch the plates, after looking closer at each powdered face. Caff laughed, but her mother didn't think it was all that funny. What kind of life was this for the girl who had everything going for her, and then some!

Sitting at the counter one day, she said that. The words popped out of her mouth, and don't take it the wrong way, she added.

When she had been told to count her blessings, to look on the bright side, Caff did the mental arithmetic, assigning a value to each blessing. This is what emerged:

She was tall, and a virgin dedicated to the Virgin from age five, from a good family, with no black marks on what the nuns called the permanent record. She had a mother who loved her, and four brothers and sisters who'd made something of themselves, but even the one marriage, Mary Ann's, had produced no children. How could that be a blessing?

Well, the mother said, it wasn't, but keep counting. What about your education and upbringing and growing up in a house owned and paid for, with room to spread out now that everyone else was gone.

"Are you counting?"

"I'm counting, but now I'm adding it all up."

"Good," said the mother, handing Caff the check, for she was the family purser.

Catherine Mary felt something stuck in her craw, and it wasn't the jelly donut soaked in coffee, or the cough drop she popped in her mouth. The licorice taste—it was the Smith Brothers, but not the wild cherry—was a shock to the palette and tongue. Now my teeth will be black, she mumbled.

"What did you say? Speak up," her mother said.

When she was little, her father would say, "stick out your tongue," and on it, he'd place a cough drop, a thin mint, a peanut, Boston baked bean, a tablet of gum—whatever he happened to have in his pajama pocket, where he kept the treats. And once— the surprise of her life—a cigarette butt, and they laughed the rest of the day, after he'd dragged her to the mirror so she could see how she looked with a "fag" hanging from her lower lip. She'd almost swallowed it, as she had the dime and penny he set there for a joke, and once had pricked her tongue with a pencil, and once covered her mouth, once he's shut it, with a kiss that was smoky and tasted of tar.

She wanted to kiss him back, but no, one was enough, don't overdo, save something for tomorrow.

He was a funny one, her daddy, an odd duck, often left out of the family fun, because never home when it was going on.

WAS HE THE LAST BLESSING? SHE LOOKED at her mother's old face, and considered. The old lady's face was like a closed book, tight and hard as a nut. The smile she cracked created a map of wrinkles, and was not convincing. It bore no relation to what was inside. Was her mother a blessing?

"Are you finished? Let's go," the face said, but Catherine Mary lingered, and forced her mother to linger by grasping her forearm and holding it to the counter, causing a fork to flip into the air, and now her mother had a yellow speck on the side of her nose.

"Kiss me," was what no one expected to hear, because they were not a family of kissing cousins, and the mother's eggy face contracted.

"Do you love me, or do you just like me?" she said to the face.

"You were always way out," said the face, "not like the rest of them. And," she continued, "you liked him better. Anyone could see that. How do you think that made me feel? Think of that, my girl, if you can stop thinking about yourself for one minute."

And now her mother had a tight grip on Catherine Mary's forearm. Her own right arm pinned down, she used her left, crossing over the right to clamp down the arm that clamped down hers.

But this was a showdown, and not a second day of days. It was a showdown and a tie, although they sat that way, clamped to each other, for fifteen long minutes. The cook didn't notice, but the waitress, holding a cake knife, saw it all.

Time stopped. And in that loose and stretchy interval, wide-open like a stream clearing its ice in one warming swell, Catherine Mary completed the action, so often begun and then aborted, started and stopped like an engine turning over, grinding with no spark of energy to become drive.

In the dark room like Aladdin's cave, she could smell her father's sleeping body—that sour, sweaty, smoky, briny fug, cooked by his hours of rest beneath the scratchy blanket he brought home from the war.

So, approaching the cot, eyes shut tight, she grabbed onto the arm he'd dropped over the side, and closed her hand around its hand. The fingers of the chemist were like pretzel rods, and she couldn't for the life of her bring one up to give it a kiss. The hand stayed where it stayed, with knuckles against the floor.

She knew before she knew that this was not Daddy's arm or his hand, and she dropped it.

Whose was it? When the soul left the body, it hovered, a gloomy lifeless cloud over the expired flesh. The body did not all die at the same time, nor did the head give up with the rest, hoarding its blood and electricity, as it said goodbye to what lay below. The skin crisped, starting with the feet and slowly cooking the legs up to the knee, and over the knee, fusing upward to the bundle of jewels, and they had a half-life longer than the limbs, but not as long as the head, so over the bundle it went, the crisping, parching arrowhead, arriving at the heart, and skipping over it, to fry up the lungs and food pipes.

The father had been dead for twenty minutes when his darling entered like a ghost to wake him. Too late. He was also dreaming, and his last dream was of the Blessed Mother, his one and only mother, whose face and hair reminded him of his baby but one. His children did not rise to welcome him in his dreams. Had he lost them?

The dream captured the slippery paces of the one coming in to wake him on his last day, the day of judgment. "Suffer the little children to come unto me," he would have whispered, or whistled, if he had a tongue in his head, but the face parts had dried and curled, and the nose and mouth, working together, could not open even a crack to admit the stale night air.

But there was something more, a warming that began in the air around him, and was his immortality, for lack of a better or more scientific name, and the soul rested on that summery cloud until it, too, darkened and chilled.

Into that cloud with the soul like an egg yoke of great price came the cruising child, who pumped his right arm (gone now, gone forever), and dropped down on him, crushing the soul into his lifeless body, squeezing it there, with no place for it to move or rise or dissipate. She watered him with her tears, and transferred morning heat, but cost him his last breath and soul's release, its transmission to where was its destiny and objective.

They were sledding together, and it was all downhill.

"Beautiful girl," were her words to herself, but they were sent by him, and to no one else.

GRACE SCHULMAN

Fireplace Bay

Where are the fires that crackled on this hill,
exciting the bay with light? The leap, the warmth,
the urgency of wood smoke, fires that singed

if you came near, that heightened conversations,
glowed on faces, shadowed sunken jaws.
The Montauk people stoked flames that warned *Danger*.

The colonists tossed seaweed over fires
for smoke that twisted into bearded clouds
and shouted across the Sound to Gardiner's Island,

food is on its way, smoke-clouds replying:
sheep's wool newly sheared, ready for transport,
and *send over clamming rakes from Parson's Smithy*.

Speak, fires. Last night a cedar fell
in the downpour, crashing power lines
that need repair; cell phones fail

without their nearby towers; computers sleep
in this speechless neighborhood. I dream of fires,
and of a surfman who recounts his catch

in stories that flare up in yellow flames
and circle into smoke. Like words.

JAMES STOTTS

sonnet for our anniversary

the sunlight is a tether
to keep me
from falling
through the heavens
baleful untamed

your eyes' sunfed shade of green
too
makes me a moon
run its race again
twelve times now

i only want
to catch some planet on the wing
in my teeth
and trot it back to you

my father's lung

i can remember the day
i found out he was dying
the stars were a machine
my phone a thing
i couldn't reach
and he wasn't anyway

it was immaterial
but i found myself imagining
the workings of a waterwheel
i couldn't tell what i was after
closure or survival
for all the things i loved

all i know or knew was
i was bound to love

though

i wasted
a gospel morning
hanging over

i soaked
until my soul
was new

waiting
for a warning
to seek cover

when and how
to say
surrender

let the body
the day
go under

listening now

for a year or so
two

until i heard
nike finally
tell me no

you must
paint your torso
blue

sonnet

i wake up to sounds
already gone forever
dawn passing over
the roofs
like a golden herd
driving westward

i try to see in
with my words
and out
with my lungs

if you still love me
it's only because
you remember me
when i was young

for j. harrison

is it wrong to reach out
at this late hour

or else you're still up
ghostwalking the dogs the crows

one last march
before you become the past

i'm scrubbing my feet clean
in the sweetgrass

sweating two days'
beer and labor

stormdoors open
wildrose drifting downstairs

radio drifting from the basement
well past two

who knows these woods are mine
but you

ROBERT WRIGLEY

Mother Country

1. BESIDES THE PEOPLE
      ...there is his knowledge of himself.
         —STEVENS

There is the fascination of a herd of elk.
About a herd of elk, which is fascinating,
there is the fascination of the elk
about the world, most especially the people,
of which, in this case, there is only one.

In the enormous eyes of the elk
a man sees the fascination he inspires,
which is particular, a secret longing
to understand both
hooflessness and lack of horns.

Precisely the mystery he too, in the midst
of a late autumn morning in the mountains,
would confront and parse.
He parts the tall grasses walking.
The elk also part the grasses walking.

There is mist in the air analogous
to nothing. There is frost
turning the seed heads and blades to minarets.
His hands, open-palmed, thumbed
to his temples, are his horns.

Everywhere the trampled spots
where the elk have bedded down
and risen from, the herd opening for him
so that he is almost elk himself among them.
He has no secrets from them.

The cows are quickened, the bulls
have put away their drive.
The winter is long and will kill one
in three and still their fascination
keeps them all where they are.

Their horns stir the mist, the cows
around the man bark in the way
of cows. The bulls neither bugle
nor prance. The man's hands flex once
and the last one still grazing looks up stunned.

If you were this man, would you sing now?
If you would, would you sing
of the scent of them, which is wild, a tincture
of stale musk, a counterpoint of fear?
Would the mist of your song join the mist in the air,

which is nothing? No matter. The thunder as they run
drums the land and the man understands
they understand his hands are hands, not horns,
and he stands, the knot at the heart of the paths
through the meadow grasses' blasted frost.

There is a world inside this world.
There is a knot, a wayward knot, not to be
undone by anyone. When they run,
the man is as alone as a star in the meadow.
The elk are dust of the star he is not.

2. PARADISE TRAILER PARK
> *...in paradise,*
> *Itself non-physical...*
> — STEVENS

Many are the places christened by men so-called,
and many are the men who would make it so,
if making were only will and hand,
ledger lines and force. Of course heaven
must have snowy mountains and saguaro,
vineyards and vivid women, not the least rumor
of televised executions nor legislative merriment,
but a blue sea, great storms, and students of the clouds.

The deer leaping back and forth across a fence
expresses a joy the bones and desiccate hide
of its fellow tangled in the strands
cannot resummon, but what is paradise
if it features no bones, no sexual innuendos
of requisite blossoms, no magisterial needs
a student of the clouds should perceive?
Heaven's perception is conceived in the flesh.

In the absence of dancing, there is violence.
The dump of empire, the backwash of Zion,
Nirvana of need, absolution in unsatisfactory ways.
The ways of the men inventing paradise
havoc cactus, its vineyards pillaged by birds.
This impoverished trailer park,
under its sagging sign, is someone's heaven,
the only child here, a boy who loves to dance.

3. JANUARY CHINOOK

> *Lakes are more reasonable than oceans.*
> — STEVENS

All day the snow fell, a foot of it
accumulated, and in the night the snow
disengaged from its geometrical designs,
becoming the most ordinary of cold rains,
and he is, in the morning, very sad.
The sodden chapeau on the weathervane,
once a mimic of the pyramidal pines,
has slumped to a watery oozing beret,
and about that he is bereft.

Still, into the deliquescing world he goes,
considering liquefaction, sentiment,
and slush, the mush his footsteps grey,
the way the just-add-water earth
dispenses scents worthy of contemplation.

Fungal things, cold meat, the *tout de suite*
too sweet life rush gushed up from death,
and he thinks, how can it be that God,
which is everything, has no mother?

And imagining everything's mother,
he imagines a God whose skin the snow was,
whose skin the meat and fungal bouquet
must be, a planetary pelvis from which
continually blossoming comes the rain.
Brew of imbroglio entered on foot,
slush slick, mud slick, a broth
of dereliction and continuity, the fact
that sadness is the fine thrum of time.

Everywhere the rat-a-tat of melts
and rivulets, tips and taps of snow wads
heavied, chunking down from pine boughs,
a raven bathing in a moss-filled tub.
In her grave, the cat's body brews
a fester round her bones. The stones
atop it mark it as a grave. The raven,
incapable of sadness, flutters a silver froth
into the air around it. So he goes walking.

Time was nothing was, which is to say
the world might be imagined, might have been
a sin everything is responsible for.
When he reaches the elephant rock, an elephant

buried the rain has half-exhumed, he sits
on the brow of what had been a great intelligence
of stone, and imagines an elephant's sadness.
The sky is a single cloud, elephant-colored.
There's a snail drowned in a depression.

More reasonable than oceans are lakes, ponds
more reasonable still, tarns in their stillness
sublime with calm. And most of all
these puddles beyond counting, one
between his boots, in which a snail is reborn,
climbing over most of an hour a single inch
onto a twig, where it raises its delicate horns
and basks like a god. Asking only that it be so,
the man is the mother of an elephant's dream.

4. LONELY SOUL

> *...the inconceivable idea of the sun.*
> — STEVENS

The whole body's phantom in the afterlife,
an indelible ache to feel felt only
as the absence of feeling. To see and taste
nothing but the memory of what had been,
to smell nothing but the scent of nothing.
Though it may be so only for the soul,

the body feeling its way into the body
of the earth, a gigantic sexual union
the soul, being bodiless, cannot conceive of.

At last the body, freed from the need
to understand, understands its need
in its own terms, while the soul imagines the nothing
of being, of being nothing more than a soul.
And yet, as the body becomes nothing,
the soul hangs on in its body's past, its fleshbook,
its pains and satisfactions, imagining,
as the body cannot, the slink of the flesh
into the afterlife, the afterlife its only witness.

Although the soul sees nothing, no taste
of the sweetness of death, no bloat, no gnaw
as the plinth of its body disintegrates—as the column
it was, from the capital vault to the spinal shaft
evaporates—and it wonders, the soul,
at the inconceivable idea of the hand.
Fine pentacular gatherer, bringer into the light
and the darkness all that once was held
for the delectation partly of the mind, the soul spark

and seed of this imagined phantomness.
Prickle of the skin, horripilation, thirst,
and tumescence, and the awareness even then

it did not feel but categorized feeling,
a taxonomer of sensation, processor of pleasure
and agony, the lonely soul vaporous
among vapors that once had had bodies too.
The ellipse of salt the fingertip was, licked
ten thousand times to turn a page.

5. BODY

> *Except when he escapes from it.*
> — STEVENS

The age of the final nostalgia, proverbs
of the pines, a mother tree the man,
having considered the risks, climbs
nevertheless, pocketing bird nests abandoned,
engaging in a momentary preachment
to an owl clenched upon a branch
draped with eviscerated hides and bones.
Who sees the tree's reality? No one
but an owl the man believes might be someone.

Near the top, the pine's main spar, clutched
between and more slender than his thighs,
sways in windlessness from his weight.
He waits and sways, then climbs two
and three more limb rungs and reaches

slowly up to stroke once the green
shivering ghost that is the topmost wisk.
He is lover of heaven and lover of earth,
in a kind of paradise, destitute and glad.

More difficult by a factor of nine
the descent, repassing the disconcerted owl
that still does not fly. By the time he reaches
earth again his gloves are gloved with pitch
and detritus, bark shards and cone grit,
an itch in his shirt where two last nests are tucked.
It may be that climbing a tree is a body's
way of understanding, climbing down
the surrender to the mind's uncertainty again.

There was almost a moment when he almost
understood his body understood the world
his imagination had laid out before him,
when what was imagined was what the body knew
and of which the imagination made its use.
It was a world there was no knowledge of
in the world, and the world was a system
he was lost in, synagogue and cathedral,
chapel in which everything that was was true.

In the homophone of its hoo, the owl pronounced
what he was, a thing alive in love with the world.
Now the wind rose and the meadow grasses

swirled and the owl soared into the distance
and vanished, in love with air, acknowledging earth.
Living where and as he lived, the man walked,
moving as a man over the body of the world
as over the body of the beloved,
something else he might never understand.

The greatest poverty was to live in the world
believing it could not be understood,
the body being one with it and the mind
believing it mattered what the mind believed:
that the earth was a place and not a destiny,
an October of the spirit, destined to be sad
but invigorated at the top of a tree,
where its body had taken it, willingly,
that it might feel and taste, hear and smell, and see.

ELIZABETH T. GRAY, JR.

Actual Things with Characteristics

FACING MEUNIÈRE FARM, FLANDERS, 18 OCTOBER 1917

BRITISH TRENCH MAP SHEET: 20 SE 3 POELCAPPELLE

V.20.A.9.1

If individuals have no psychic or magical abilities
then actual things with characteristics,
such as the four elements, hail, poison, boils, precipices,
and so on, become obstacles.

Whenever such forms arise
remain in a state
of detachment and integrate them
into your path as illusions.

Yesterday, when actual things with characteristics arose,
a detachment tried to integrate them into its path
as illusions, but the actual things with characteristics
were stubborn and well-led.

Chilled Feet

Chilled feet and frostbite
are caused by prolonged standing
in cold water and mud
were our constant companions.
These conditions can be prevented or diminished
by means of improved trench construction; by reducing
the time spent in trenches; by movement;
by the provision of warmth, shelter, hot food,
and facilities for washing the feet and drying wet clothes
were nowhere to be found.
Boots, socks, and puttees are to be removed
at least once in twenty-four hours, the feet rubbed
for twenty minutes, dried, greased with whale oil,
and a dry pair of socks put on, if available.
On no account must the feet be held near a fire
would have been a godsend
nor must hot water be used.

Recognizing the Signs of Death

44TH CASUALTY CLEARING STATION, POPERINGHE,

SEPTEMBER 1917

BRITISH TRENCH MAP SHEET: 27 L.10.B.3.5

dreaming of being led by a man on foot
or on a horse, toward the west

in the shade of trees, where one cannot
be escorted by others, and once there

hearing someone crying behind one

then the rustle of stiff cloth, light breaking,
the muffled sound of metal on metal

a woman nearby carries burning twigs of juniper
and a mirror

Preliminary Orders

FOR SECOND ARMY, X CORPS, 21ST DIVISION,
62ND INFANTRY BRIGADE, 1 OCTOBER 1917
BRITISH TRENCH MAP SHEET: 28 NE 1 ZONNEBEKE D.16.C
(EAST OF BOURDEAUX FARM)

The two lead companies will advance as light
as possible and thus will not carry shovels.

Nothing superfluous will be taken. No greatcoats
at Zero. Wire is reported to be light.

Bayonets will not be fixed
if there is moonlight.

Protecting walls must be built for the horses at once.
The men may dig down or build walls for themselves.

If the two lead companies advance as light
they will not need to advance as something else,

as men or fodder or exhortation or as a dark wing
that strains to unpin itself from wet ground.

If in moonlight bayonets will not be fixed
they can remain fluid, imagining themselves

as silver fear or unborn phosphor or even the wire out there
that is also reported to be light.

~~

At Zero the warm enormous horses
will shrug their great coats behind protecting walls.

Try to imagine that the men will not need
to dig or build, but simply,

as the flares and star shells do,
advance as light.

Sound Ranging

The colonel
was confusing
the shock wave
caused by the shell
passing at more
than the speed of
sound with the sound
of the gun
itself.
    The way
in certain circumstances
abdominal recoil
is mistaken
for grief: shock
preceding report.

Notes on Sources

"Actual Things With Characteristics." The first two stanzas draw from Sarah Harding's translation of a twelfth-century Tibetan text, *Machik's Complete Explanation: Clarifying the Meaning of Chöd*. Boston, Massachusetts: Shambala, 2013.

"Chilled Feet." Much of the text draws from *63rd (Royal Naval) Division Standing Trench Orders*. London: The War Office, 1917.

"Recognizing the Signs of Death." Much of the text draws from *Namchur Mingur Dorje: The Interpretation of Dreams in a 17th Century Tibetan Text*, Robin Cook and Enrico Dell'Angelo, trans. Arcidosso, Italy: Shang Shung Edizioni, 1996.

"Preliminary Orders." The first section draws from the original text of these orders. Collection of the Imperial War Museum, London.

"Sound Ranging." Sound ranging is a method of determining the geographical coordinates of a hostile enemy battery by using data derived from microphones in multiple locations, each of which produces a bearing to the source of the sound. The text of this poem draws from *Artillery's Astrologers*, by Peter Chasseaud, Lewes, UK: Mapbooks, 1999.

The geographical coordinates in the poems use the trench map grid system developed by the British Royal Survey Corps in 1914 and 1915 and used throughout World War I.

MARIA STEPANOVA

TRANSLATED BY SASHA DUGDALE

*Last Songs (*from *Kireevsky)*

The last songs are assembling,
Soldiers of a ghostly front:
Escaping from surrounded places
A refrain or two make a break for it
Appearing at the rendez-vous
Looking about them, like the hunted.

How stiffly unbending they are
Running water won't soften them now!
How unused they are to company
The words don't form as they ought.
But their elderly, skillful hands
Pass the cartridges round,
And until first light their seeing fingers
Reassemble Kalashnikovs,
They draw, with sharp intake of breath
From wounds, the deeply lodged letters—
And towards morning, avoiding checkpoints,
They enter the sleepless city.

In times of war, they fall silent.
When the muses roar, they fall silent.

BOŻENA KEFF

TRANSLATED BY BENJAMIN PALOFF AND ALISSA VALLES

Persephone

In the backwaters of depression she lies half-sunken, her open maw
full of complaint—sometimes a tongue of hot lava—sometimes a
   scattering
of cold ash from the archives of the Jewish Historical Institute,
where, sorting through the shot and the gassed,
she stumbled on something.
"I found," says she, looking
straight into the void (which is me, on a chair), "a document.
My mother was killed in a forest outside Lvov.
She was shot in the forest. Half a century, and I didn't know."

For half a century she didn't know, and now she knows.
And she speaks of it in the presence of a random witness.
In point of fact, a brunette in crocodile-skin gloves,
agent from the world of make-believe, Lara Croft, or some such,
who's firing up her Cessna in Hawaii when an old maid
in a threadbare cloak gets snagged in the propeller. Lara climbs out
to help the poor thing, who, eyes cast into the void, informs her
that half a century ago her mother was shot in the forest.

"How horrible!"
cries Lara, for she is not without a heart.

The birthplace of the goddess is Lvov. Nola, forced out
from this nest by an angry Angra Mainyu
by the name of Hitler, had to go east, deep into Russia,
to towns and cities, all the way to the Urals, with her friend,
and it's thanks to her, she herself admits, that she survived.

Russia stretches far to the east and is being evacuated there,
except for those sent to Siberia, like Nola's brother, unbeknownst to
    her.
For now she tears forward—behind her the army of Angra Mainyu
    makes chase, infantry,
air power, armor—demons from the west in trucks, in jeeps,
on motorcycles, and on foot, in good boots, yet
leaving a trail of corpses, of her kind and others', and onward, and
    onward;
Nola crams herself into freight cars with everyone else,
she works in factories, sews, gets typhus, starves, and again flees
by train across the steppes, and over the trains the feathered snake of
    the Luftwaffe
uncurls its tail strafes locomotives stops scatters their cars,
then hunts the people, dives drives takes aim; it's Soweto here it's a
    safari!

However many the Angras Mainyu have hunted and devoured, they
    want more, they spit bones hair shoes,
they erect gallows light fires happily sing cry themselves laughing,
so radiant do they feel in this radical bestiality, this cadaverous decay,
they sing until their maws are filled with snow metal and hunger.

As for Nola, after the war she returned to a country she hadn't
    lived in before.
To strange cities, where she would meet Aura's father, also from
    Lvov.
He'd just returned from Berlin, from the lair of Angra Mainyu,
    whom he'd crushed,
and brought back his only sewing machine for Nola.

With the People's Army,
which blossoms from the "hours of our friendship,"
he traversed half of Europe
and felt that he, too, belonged to the People, to the People of Earth,
    to the People of the Planet,
to Equality, Liberty, free education, and agricultural reform,
but in time he was mortally disappointed

(though that's a different story).

～～

"They'll come from the west, they'll arrive in tanks and cars,
and I, and crowds, and crowds of people, onto the train,
flee to the east!" Meter's voice screams, she's whirling within it
like a dervish, always like a top in circles.
She will never cross this time horizon.
"But I thought my mother was safe! That my brother and sister… !
And the whole time there was no one left."
She says. *"No one."* She repeats, repeats

and looks into that lack of meaning—
because it's not into fate (and on this we agree).

"So you mean my grandmother," Aura says, "you mean my aunt."
"Grandmother?" Meter repeats. "Have you lost your marbles? What
    did these heroes
have to do with you, kid? This story happened to me.
I had to live through it.
You have Nothing to do with Anything."

METER
Now that Hitler, who murdered my family,
And Stalin, may they both rot in Hell, are dead,
You're all I have left, my child,
Of those I have loved.

Aura's hair is now grey, but, unlike her mother, she dyes it.
Aura visits her after a long absence to see how her mother's
getting on in life, in this, the new age's old age.
They've sipped their tea, sit quietly, watch TV
about their country. They're erecting a monument to Dmowski.
    Mother says: look,
everywhere, bastard Fascism, always these bastards.
When I was young, they ran through Lvov with razors and slashed
    Jews,

now the Jews are all gone, all killed, the rest driven out. I regret
    having stayed
(though what do you do people are stupid helpless idiotic).
But for these nationalists nothing's changed. They appoint their own
    Jews.
Their morality is something that allows them to slash others with
    razors,
that's all they get out of it, and again they're rinsing their mouths
from morning to night with fatherland and god. They don't deserve
    a single Jew here,
whatever his nation, gender, orientation, or skin color.
I have no idea how decent people get on
in this country, perhaps when Europe opens up they'll leave,
or they must suffer. I, for my part, as you know, believe in no god.
I'm a realist; self-delusion is, in my circumstances, beneath me.
Believe me. Maybe I talk about it too much, but I've lived through
    too much, too.

To which Aura says: Being Persephone, I agree with you, Hecate,
And I must declare you to be a person of honor.

ROSANNA WARREN

The Mud Hole

I.
The pit, the sump, childhood's dark
pond nestled at the bottom of the hill.
Frog spawn bubbled on glossy black.
The green frog blinked on a stone. A snake
eased through weeds, slid into murk.
A cardinal sliced the air. I sat
in the crotch of the maple over the pond,
bare legs dangling, for hours. Hours
I watched, waiting for signs.
No one found me, alone in my tree.
My skin grew bark, I murmured spells
never to grow old, or up, or reasonable,
or tall. A spotted turtle crawled
up the bank and turned to stone, and all
afternoon was noon, no aftering, as sun
through leaves on rippled shadow fell.

II.
And history? We studied history. It had stopped.
So said Miss Gould, Fourth Grade. "We" had won
the War. World War. Now Peace would last
forever. Korea wouldn't be on the test.
Vietnam was a distant, insignificant noise.
Bells rang. Obediently, we crouched
under our desks, hands on our heads, and thought
Peace must be like an infinite recess,

and soon we could scramble up and go to lunch.
Until that day someone interrupted class
with a message for Miss Gould. She read, turned white.
"Children," she said. "Children, the President—"
She paused. We waited. Miss Gould cleared her throat:
"The President has had an accident."

III.

Oh, the cheese boards, the little scimitars
with china handles for slicing camembert,
the craze for *fondue*, parties bristling with spears
like Paolo Uccello—anything to hold off
the body counts, the spectral photographs
of flaming villages, the marches in some far-off
mythological, mankind-mangling South,
kiosks torched in Harvard Square, cars upside down,

a decade choked in tear gas. The bottle spun,
darkened basements spun as tongue met tongue.
The moon spun under our boot treads. We were young.
Beans sprouted tiny croziers. Our utopias

would replace the old. Never at a loss
for heaven on earth, America,
we wreathed you in incense and alstromeria,
our diaphragms swam in spermicide. We were free,

we made free. Money whistled through our hands.
We tended the candle flame of innocence
and blithely, blindly, thickened toward the dark.
Smoke in our eyes. On our lips, a lullaby.

LES MURRAY

Continuous Creation

We bring nothing into this world
except our gradual ability
to create it, out of all that vanishes
and all that will outlast us.

Parental Job Swap

Sitting next to his flagon
on the morning stairs,
his wife on the bus
lovingly escaping eight children.

He hiccups the courage to go
to his emptied duties
and stay drunk enough to hold on
there while assuring dismissal—

he remembers that his wife
has finally taken her own job
and the bus, continually promoted,
dark jacket to silk-cream jacket,

rumbles like his gut in the day.
He, falling over his flagon,
has suffered the good disaster
as his wife is promoted yet again

through the roof, above the children
who had been shielding him
as he dreams unpaid FM
world music; ee limo limo

her bus has been promoted
to two teenagers driving him
in her limo to his shrink
in hiccups, to drain his flagon.

KAREN LEONA ANDERSON

From

Mice slipping from the Nile, half mud.
Roaches and bats. Love from an egg,
the wild ducks cracking out from the barnacles,
bees from dead steers, flies, crocodiles.
The time of the singing has come—
muscling up, the doves, split and clapped
hot on the feet of the afflicted, rising up
as if winged, as if the lark could rip
from its music and fall away. Nothing
comes from nothing, the birds don't make milk
except the pigeons born from their own food,
our mothers honey and lowering knives.
No evil can arise from a little wooled sheep
or a sleek grey bird. A sacrifice, a man whose facts
cannot be checked says he can hear something
inside a melon and cracks it and there is a lamb,
miraculous except that its feet are green
and rooted to the ground.

Honey

Star spit, heaven's sweat, the excrement
of god and insect. Light's night. Forget
the sweetness and everything's vomit.
When can we eat. When the water's
mixed with gall, when the child shrieks
the morning into endtimes, and upsets
the bowl on the table, a bright curse
for the things you didn't get, better cereal,
a cloud, a crown of fair green barley,
wet with insecticides. You see that this is right
as fungus is, always growing. We're going to be,
the curse continues, I promise, worse than late,
the sugar soaked in blood and ashes,
and honey still in the shoes and clothes
and spoons and buttons, the colony collapsed.
Muse, shall we sing of cane? You see that
won't be cleaned up, the wrongs in what you eat
and what you breathe and where you came from.
Forever sticky, enzymed, your endearments,
history's waste, and it leaks over
the edge of the table, golden and indelible,
may the stars piss down and the gods
will come as bees, as thick as rain.

Dollhouse

These are the girls who want a house, a place
exactly as hard as the houses they see in their
minds, of steel and wood, now capable of grandeur,
now of gravity. They do not think, as you would,
of the things found not to scale, the dolls too big,
the toilet brimming with glue, no paper,
the windows glassless, the people stiff astride
the chairs, their clothes so crudely sewn
their collars choke them up. They'll tell
you what's wrong: the flat blankets and the TV won't
turn on, everyone is watching stone-
faced and everyone is resting on their backs
in their separate rooms. It's the house
of the accident, the house in which the silverfish
come long as snakes, the cockroaches dogs,
the mice like bears raiding the polyester
fill of the beds, eating the wallpaper glue.
Something slow has been happening all along,
not horror but the plaster ham up in the attic
wracked, the slurry of rain and gnats cupped in the sink.
It can't be turned away: the house dissolving
in the grass and in the grass, the ants.

FRIEDRICH HÖLDERLIN

TRANSLATED BY BRUCE LAWDER

The Rhine

FOR ISAAC VON SINCLAIR

I sat in the dark ivy, at the gateway
Of the forest, at the time when golden noon
There visiting the source descended
From the steps of the Alpine mountains,
For me the godly built,
The castle of the heavenly
According to tradition, but where
Secretly still much that is decisive
Comes down to people; from there
I knew without surmise
A fate, for hardly was
I in the warm shade
Debating with myself when my soul
Wandered to Italy
And further to the coast of Moreas.

But now amidst the mountains,
Far below the silver summits
And below the friendly green
Where the forests shuddering at him
And the faces of cliffs, one above another,
Look down, all day, there
In the coldest abyss I heard
Him wailing for deliverance,
The youth, they heard him, how he raged,
Accusing Mother Earth
And the Thunderer, who begot him,

His parents, pitying, yet
Mortals fled from the place,
For it was dreadful as without light
He twisted in his chains
The raving of the demigod.

The voice it was of the most noble river,
The free-born Rhine's,
And something else he hoped for as above there from his
  brothers,
The Ticino and the Rhône,
He parted and desired to wander and impatient
Toward Asia then his kingly soul drove him.
Yet injudicious is
The wish ahead of fate.
The blindest however
Are the sons of the gods. For a man knows
His house and the animal where
It should build, yet theirs is
The fault that they don't know for what purpose
To the inexperienced soul it is given.

A riddle is the source-sprung. Even
The hymn dare hardly disclose it. For
As you begin so you remain,
As much as need
And nurture act, most namely
Birth accomplishes

And the light-ray which
Greets the new-born.
But where is there one
To remain free
His whole life, and to fulfill
The heart's wish alone, from such
Propitious heights, as the Rhine,
And from such a sacred womb
Happily born, as that one?

Thus exultation's his word,
Nor does he as other children like
To cry in swaddling-bands;
For where the banks at first
Creep to his side, the crooked ones,
And thirstily winding round him,
The thoughtless one, desire
To guide and carefully guard him
In their own teeth, laughing
He rips off the coils and rushes away
With his prey and if in his hurry
A greater force does not tame him, but
Lets him grow, like lightning must he
Split the earth, and as if charmed the forests
Flee after him as well as the mountains collapsing.

A god however wants to spare the sons
A hurried life and smiles
When intemperate but restrained
By the sacred Alps the rivers
Rage at him from their depths, like that one.
In such a forge then
Even everything pure is hammered
And it is beautiful how he then
After quitting the mountains
And quietly wandering through German lands
Contents himself and stills his longing
In useful action when he builds the land,
Now Father Rhine, and nourishes lovely children
In cities which he has founded.

Yet never, never does he forget it.
For sooner shall the dwelling perish
And the laws and the day of man
Become as nothing before such a one
Dare forget the origin
And the pure voice of youth.
Who was it then who first
Corrupted the lines of love
And out of them made bonds?
Then the defiant mocked
Their own rights and certain
Of the heavenly fire, only then
Despising mortal paths,

Chose what was arrogant
And strove to become the equals of gods.

They have however enough
Of their own immortality, the gods, and if
The heavenly need one thing
It is heroes and human beings
And other mortals. For as
The most blessèd feel nothing of themselves,
Another, if indeed such may
Be said, must, in the name of the gods,
Participatingly feel,
Him they need; however their rule
Is that he break his own house
And scorn what he most loves
As the enemy and bury father and child
Under the rubble
Should he desire to be as they and not
Bear difference, the dreamer.

Thus happy he who finds
A well-allotted fate,
Where still the memory
Of wanderings and, sweetly, of sufferings
Resounds on the sure shore
That there and yonder happily
He may look as far as the bounds
Which at his birth God

Drew for his sojourn.
Then he's at peace, blessèdly modest,
For all that he desired,
What's heavenly, of itself embraces
Unforced, smiling,
Now that he's at peace, the bold one.

Demigods I think of now
And I must know the dear ones,
Since often their lives have
So moved my yearning heart.
But that man whose soul, Rousseau,
Like yours, became invincible,
The strongly enduring,
Whose mind was sure
And who had the sweet gift of listening,
Of speaking so that from sacred profusion he,
Like the wine-god, foolishly divine
And lawless, gives it, the language of the purest,
Comprehensible to the good, but as is right
Strikes the disrespectful with blindness,
The desecrating servants, how should I name that stranger?

The sons of Earth are, like the Mother,
All-loving, thus they also receive,
Without effort, the fortunate ones, everything.
That's why it also surprises
And startles the mortal man
When he thinks of the heavens

Which he with loving arms
Has heaped onto his shoulders
And of the burden of joy;
Then often it seems best
To be almost forgotten
There where the ray does not sear,
In the shade of the woods
By Lake Bienne amidst fresh verdure,
And carefree poor to learn,
Beginner-like, tones from the nightingale.

And glorious it is then from sacred sleep
To rise and from the forest's coolness
Awaking, evening now,
To near the milder light
When he who built the mountains
And drew the path of the rivers,
After he smiling had also
Steered the active life
Of mankind, the poor-in-breath,
Like sails with his own breezes,
Is at peace, too, and to the pupil now,
Finding more good
Than evil, the shaping one,
Day bows down to the earth.——

Then men and gods celebrate marriage,
All of the living celebrate,
And for a while

Fate is in balance.
And the fugitives seek the inn,
And sweet slumber the brave,
The lovers however
Are what they were, they are
At home, where the flower delights
In harmless ardor and round the dark trees
The spirit rustles, the unreconciled
However are transformed and hurry
To hold out to each other their hands
Before the friendly light
Goes under and the night comes.

Yet for some
This hurries past quickly, others
Retain it longer.
The eternal gods are
Vital forever; unto death
However even a man can
Still retain in the mind what's best
And then he experiences the highest.
Only each has his measure.
For unhappiness is hard
To bear, but harder happiness.
A wise man however
From midday to midnight
And till morning's first gleam
Could at the banquet stay lucid.

To you upon the hot path under pines or
Within the dark of the oak woods wrapped
In steel, my Sinclair! may God appear or
In clouds, you will know Him, since from your youth you have
   known
The Good One's power, and never from you
Is hidden the smile of the Ruler
By day when
All that lives seems feverish and fettered
Or also
By night when everything is
Mixed orderless and there returns
Primeval confusion.

The Only One

(first version)

What is it that
Binds me to the ancient
Blessèd coasts, so that I love
Them still more than my own country?
For as into celestial
Captivity sold
I am there, where Apollo went
In the form of a king,
And to innocent youth
Zeus came down and in sacred art
Begot sons and daughters,
The Exalted, among mankind.

Of exalted thoughts
Namely have many
Sprung from the Father's head
And great souls
Come from Him to mankind.
I have heard
Of Elis and Olympia, have
Stood upon Parnassus,
And above the mountains of the Isthmus,
And also over
By Smyrna and down
By Ephesus have I gone;

Much that is beautiful have I seen,
And I have sung

God's image, which lives among
Mankind, and still,
You ancient gods and all
You valiant sons of the gods,
Still one I seek, whom
I love among you,
Where you conceal the last of your kind,
The treasure of the house,
From me, the foreign guest.

My master and lord!
O you, my teacher!
What in the distance
Have you remained? and when
I asked among the ancients,
The heroes and
The gods, why did you stay
Away? And now full
Of sorrow is my soul,
As if even you cried, you heavenly ones,
That, should I serve one,
The other would fail me.

I know, however, it is my own
Fault! For too much,
O Christ, do I hang on you,
Although as Hercules' brother
And bold I recognize you, you

Are also Evius' brother, the one
Who to the wagon spanned
The tigers and then down
Unto the Indus
Commanding joyful service
Founded the vineyard and
Tamed the wrath of the peoples.

A shame however hinders me
From comparing you to
The worldly men. And surely I
Know He who begot you, your Father,
The same one who[...]

For He never reigns alone.

Love however hangs
On one. This time
Namely too much from my own heart
Has the hymn gone,
I want to make good the fault
When I sing still others.
I never reach, as I wish,

The measure. A god however knows
When it comes, what I wish, the best.
For as the master
Wandered on earth,
A captive eagle,

And many who
Saw him feared for their lives,
Meanwhile the Father did
His utmost and His best
Really wrought among mankind,
And very sad was also
The Son for long until He
Ascended to heaven through the air,
Like Him the soul of the heroes is captive.
The poets must,
The spiritual, too, be of this world.

Patmos

For the Landgrave of Homburg

Near and
Hard to grasp is God.
But where danger is grows
Deliverance, too.
In darkness dwell
The eagles and fearless go
The sons of the Alps over the abyss
On light-built bridges.
Therefore, since all around are heaped
The summits of time, and the most loved
Live near, growing weary on
Most separated mountains,
Give innocent water,
O give us wings, most faithful sense
To cross over and back again.

Thus I spoke as there carried me off
Faster than I had surmised
And far, where I had never
Thought to come, a spirit
From my own house. There glimmered
In twilight, as I went,
The shadowy forest
And the yearning brooks
Of home; no longer did I know these lands;
Yet soon in growing splendor,

Mysterious
In golden smoke, there blossomed
Quickly grown high
With steps of the sun, fragrant
With a thousand summits,

Asia, and, dazzled, I sought
One thing that I might know, for unaccustomed
Was I to the wide ways, where downwards
From Tmolus comes
The gold-bedecked Pactolus
And Taurus stands and Messogis,
And full of flowers the garden,
A silent fire, however in light
High up there blossoms the silver snow,
And witness to immortal life
On inaccessible walls
Pristine the ivy grows and there are borne
By living columns, cedar and laurel,
The festive,
The divinely constructed palaces.

There murmur however round Asia's gates
Extending here and there
On the uncertain plain of the sea
Of the shadowless streets enough,

Yet he knows the islands, the boatman.
And when I heard
One of the near
Was Patmos,
Much did I want
To put in there, and there
To approach the dark cavern.
For not, like Cyprus,
The rich-in-sources, or
One of the others, does
Patmos spendidly dwell,

But in the poorer house
She is hospitable
Nonetheless
And when after shipwreck or lamenting
His homeland or
A departed friend,
One of the foreign
Approaches, she listens gladly, and her children,
The voices of the fiery grove,
Even where the sand falls and the field's
Surface cracks, the sounds,
They listen to him and lovingly all resounds
Again with the man's laments. So once
She tended him, the one God loved,
The seer, who in blessèd youth

Went with
The son of the Almighty, inseparable, for
He loved, the Thunder-bearer, the simplicity
Of the disciple and he saw, the mindful man,
The face of God exactly,
When, by the mystery of the vine, they
Sat down together, at the hour of the meal,
And in the great soul, calmly divining, death
The Lord announced and the ultimate love, for never enough
Of words had He to speak
Of kindness, then, and to brighten, as
He saw it, the wrath of the world.
For everything is good. With this He died. Much could
Be said of that. And they saw Him, how He looked, triumphantly,
Most joyful still, the friends, there at the end,

And yet they mourned, as it
Was evening now, amazed,
For what was greatly determined they had in their souls,
The men, however under the sun they loved
Life and did not want to leave
The face of the Lord
And their homeland. Thrust in,
Like fire in iron, was that, and beside them went
The Loved One's shade.
Thus He sent them
The Spirit, and surely the house
Quaked and the storm of God rolled down

Far-thundering over
The divining heads, as, hard-in-thought,
The heroes of death were gathered together,

Now that He departing
Still once more appeared to them.
For now the day put out the sun,
The Kingly One, and broke in pieces
The straightly radiating
Scepter, divinely suffering, of His own will,
For it should come again,
At the right time. Good would it not
Have been, later, and would abruptly have broken off,
    unfaithfully,
The people's work, and joy it was
From now on
To dwell in loving night, and preserve
In simple eyes, resolute,
Abysses of wisdom. And there also grew green
Deep in the mountains living images,

Yet terrible it is how here and there
Ceaselessly God disperses the living.
For already to leave the face
Of the dear friends
And go far off over the mountains

Alone, where doubly
Recognized, unanimous
Was the Heavenly Spirit; and not prophesied was it, rather
It took them by the hair, precisely then,
When suddenly
God looked back, and swearing
So He would stay, calling
Evil goldenly bound henceforth
As with ropes, they held out to each other their hands—

But when there dies the One
Beauty depended
On most, so that in that form
A miracle occurred and the heavenly pointed
At Him, and when, eternal riddle for each other,
They cannot grasp
Each other who once lived together
In remembrance, and not the sand alone or
The willows does it bear away and seizes
The temples, but the honor
Of the demigod and his followers
Decays and even His face
The Almighty turns
Away, so that no longer is
There an immortal to see in heaven or
On green earth, what is this?

It is the casting of the sower when he takes
With the shovel the wheat
And casts it toward the light, swinging it over the threshing-
    floor.
The chaff falls to his feet, however
The grain reaches its end,
And not an evil is it if a little
Goes lost and from the word
The living sound dies away,
For divine work also resembles our own,
Not everything does the Almighty will at once.
True, the pit bears iron,
And glowing resin Etna,
Thus I should have means
To make an image and see
Him much as He was, Christ.

If one however spurred himself on,
And, sadly speaking, on the move, when I was defenseless,
Accosted me, so that I stood astonished and, a servant,
Desired to imitate God's image—
In wrath once visible I saw
The Lord of Heaven, not that I should be something, rather
To learn. Benevolent they are, but what they most abhor is,
As long as they reign, what's false, and then
No longer is what's human valid among humans.
For they don't rule, what rules is
The fate of immortals, and their work moves

Of itself and hastening reaches its end.
When namely the heavenly triumphal procession
Goes higher, there will be named, like the sun,
By the strong the jubilant Son of the Highest,

A watchword-sign, and here is the staff
Of the hymn, beckoning downwards,
For nothing is common. The dead
He awakens, those not yet caught
By coarseness. There wait however
Of the shy eyes many
To see the light. They do not want
To blossom on the burning ray,
Although the golden bridle restrains their courage.
But when, as if
From darkened orbs
Oblivious of the world,
Quietly illuminating force falls from holy scripture, they,
Glad of grace, may practice
Upon the quiet gaze.

And if the heavenly now,
As I believe, love me,
How much more you,
For one thing I know,
That namely the will
Of the eternal Father is
Valid for you. Silent is His sign

On the thundering heaven. And one stands under it
His whole life long. For Christ still lives. The heroes, however,
   his sons,
Have all come and the holy scripture
About Him and the deeds of the earth
Explain the lightning till now,
A footrace not to be stopped. But He is there. For all His works
   are
Known unto Him from the beginning.

Too long, too long now has
The honor of the heavenly been invisible.
For they must almost lead
Our fingers and ignominiously
A violence tears at our hearts.
For each of the heavenly demands sacrifice,
When one however was neglected,
Good never came of it.
We have served Mother Earth
And recently the sunlight,
Unknowing, but what the Father, Who
Reigns over all, most loves
Is that the solid letter
Be cared for and what exists well
Interpreted. This German hymn follows.

Remembrance

The northeaster blows,
The dearest of winds
To me, because of the fiery spirit
And good voyage it promises sailors.
Go now however and greet
The beautiful Garonne
And the gardens of Bordeaux
There, where by the rugged bank
The path goes hither and into the river
The brook drops deeply, above however
Look out a noble pair
Of oaks and silver poplars;

I still remember that and how
The elm wood bows
Its broad crown over the mill,
In the courtyard however a fig tree grows.
On holidays
Tanned the women go
On silken ground,
In March,
When night and day are equal,
And over slow pathways,
Laden with golden dreams,
Lulling breezes drift.

Give me, however,
Full of the dark light

The fragrant cup
That I might rest; for sweet
In the shade would be slumber.
It is not good
Soulless to be free
Of mortal thoughts. Yet a talk
Is good and to speak
The heart's truth, to hear much
Of the days of love
And things that happened.

Where however are the friends? Bellarmine
With his companion? Many
Shy off from going to the source;
For wealth namely begins
In the sea. They,
Like painters, bring together
The beauty of the earth and do
Not scorn winged war, and
To live lonely, year-long, below
The leaf-stripped mast, where through the night do not shine
The holidays of the city,
Nor lyres nor native dance.

Now however to Indians
The men have gone,
There from the airy point
By the vineyards, where downwards

The Dordogne comes,
And together with the splendid
Garonne sea-wide
The river moves out. It takes, however,
And gives remembrance, the sea,
And love, too, keenly focuses the eyes.
What stays, however, the poets found.

To Zimmer

The lines of life are various,
As pathways are, and as the mountains' limits.
What here we are can there a god complete
With harmony and eternal reward and peace.

HOWARD ALTMANN

The Birds

It was hard to see; it was hard to see.
Everything was hard to see.
The breeze had made things clearer for a bit.
The sun had made things worse for long stretches.
Twilight swept it all into a ball, worn and frayed.
That's what the mind saw, clouded as it was.

Meaning was having a rough go of it.
It didn't know where to shine its shoes.
Which corners needed dusting.
A reason to draw the shades.
It was asking to be rejected.
And it was, over and over.

The bird on the wire had the answer.
She knew to stay just long enough to stay.
When she returned, she returned with a friend.
And the darkening blue sky inched closer.
"Listen here," it said.
"I will lose these, too."

Who could ask for anything more?
I held my place.
The taking off, the arrival.
The taking off.
Come night, come hither—
The island had me on a line.

The ocean must've known to hang in there.
Staying on voice.
Closing in on its song.
Rinsing the sand from its mouth.
The earth was moving; the earth was moving.
Everything was moving.

The Man at the Hotel Bar

The man at the hotel bar was thinking of palm trees.
A low-hanging bulb burnished green apples in a bowl.
In an adjacent square skaters circled Portugal's last king.
Silent Night edged the surrounding hills.
A one-legged woman jiggled a sock of coins.
Knitting stars was a Lisbon sky.

These are the facts.
Moved to toast them were the distillers of emotion.
The painter of lonely faces brushed the man up in skates.
The writer of sad songs penned the woman stuffing apples in a
   sock.
In their room they shared their wanderings.
In the corridor of spouses: *please do not disturb.*

And in the passage of the sun Fado doesn't fade.
As the blues don't become bluer at night.
For the light of day is the art of darkness.
The fugue of painter and writer the dream.
The leaning this way and that a reality.
The man at the hotel bar was thinking of palm trees.

DEREK WALCOTT

Milky Way

A tenor pan repeating its high note,
flowers of brass cornets, maracas stars,
an alto sax's interrupting throat,
a burst of rain from drizzling guitars.

Music of the Future

Wide over the water, but gentle, the night music
requires the sad stars' accompaniment,
note, true, by sparkling note, and then, a cluster,
a single note spreads to a constellation,
the bass breathes evenly a steady luster,
first a few stars and then a constellation,
first the breaker's slow clapping, and then, the ovation.

Pelican Island

Looking for anchor in a Rothko sky
and a bay below like a basin of blood—
"We used to come here at dusk to watch them
roost by the score, here there's only one?
Where did they all go?" I asked Robert Devaux.
"The pelicans?" he asked. "I'll tell you."
He was a lovely man who loved the island
"Insecticides," he said. He's gone too.

Pelican Man

Caught by an electric flash that startles a fence
of blue coconuts, the half-nude, bearded
poacher is startled by our presence
on the night beach without the beaded
weight of the pelican he has killed. You know those scenes
in a cop movie where during the bank heist
a flash like this reveals the bandit's face
and he half-audibly mutters "Jesus Christ"
as the far, faint sirens start. In Chekhov's The Seagull
the girl, Nina, is compared to the broken bird. There is no gull
in one of the paintings, but its absence is beautiful.
We have done things to nature in our time.
The victim may be missing, but not the crime.

In the Heart of Old San Juan

To me, the waking day is Margaret:
down every street, every street corner,
the boulevards brilliant, with one regret;
every memory is now a mourner.
On the day of a reception for her death
Peter came to her house; there was the usual
chaos of friends, faces against the bright earth
of Santa Cruz; daughters, granddaughters.
Margaret was gone but all the streets were hers,
sunlight down White Street down by the Little Carib or
the talkative reflections in the harbor—
all these are her monuments, not paint or verse.

Paramin

She loved to say it and I loved to hear it,
"Paramin," it had the scent of cocoa in it,
the criss-crossing trunks of leafy gommiers straight
out of Cézanne and Sisley, the road rose then fell fast
into the lush valley where my daughters live.
The name said by itself could make us laugh
as if some deep, deep secret was hidden there.
I see it through crossing tree trunks framed with love
and she is gone but the hill is still there
and when I join her it will be Paramin
for both of us and the children, the mountain air
and music with no hint of what the name could mean,
rocking gently by itself, "Paramin," "Paramin."

Lapeyrouse Umbrella

Her merciless absence multiplies my thoughts,
while three pouis are blooming on Pigeon Island
above the triangular sails of the regatta yachts.
Another glittering day without you; take my hand
and bring me to wherever we were: the empty house
in Petit Valley or the city of Lapeyrouse
where headstones multiply like sails on a Sunday,
where a widower tacks under a pink parasol,
where people think pain or pan is good for the soul.
You go down Tragarete Road to enter Saint James.
What she has forgotten you learn every day, Peter.
It is a country full of paintable names:
Paramin, Fyzabad, Couva, where the trees rhyme.
She sleeps in that country where there is no time,
as my pen and your brushstroke blend in the one meter.

SUSAN WHEELER

History of the Anti-Papacy

"Feelings are not faith," the priest Molly said to me one day
when I was trying to talk about god as casually as I might the
dishes. Some years later in an adjacent room the priest Roger
wrote a book about faith and the five senses, but I knew what
Molly meant. A school bell rang and voices wafted over her
wooden desk like the helicopter seeds of a maple tree along with
an occasional acorn. "Molly," I said, "how can you tell zinnias
from echinacea?" Speaking of seeds.

My Brother Jasper

You got to wake up with motivation. That's why they call it
Lent—cuz it will have LENT you the will of another. 'Til you
become dependent on that will, like a splint or a crutch, a good
crutch, or like a tool. A hammer you could not build a house
without, at least a house that kept out the water and wind, or
at least the wind. As long as you're building it out of lumber,
out of planed lumber, like from a lumber yard, you know, not
logs that you can notch without nails and get a pretty tight fit.
The other whose will it lends you you might think of as god, or
Mike's cousin who got that green job in Lincoln, or just the guys
you rock those pickup games with. Or remember that kid Bruce
you did that salt paste volcano with, you *lived* that volcano, man.
You guys were going to take it to the museum, you thought
it was that good, you were going to donate it to them if they
guaranteed they'd have it in the lobby in one of those glass
boxes. Like a Swatch watch, like those plastic boxes a Swatch
comes in, only bigger. That would have looked great. You got
to remember how you felt about that volcano. Like the fuse
you used is in you now to ignite you but it will never burn you
up, not even itself up, it will just keep igniting you until April
and—then you've got it made, you're in the home stretch, man,
you're around the corner from every beer you want.

Not Ideas About the Thing but the Thing-Not-Idea

The kid in his body moved like a robot
    [seems like a sound in his mind]
that motion, morph, warp jagged
    [a bird's cry at daybreak / sunup]
beat-box before school, box-beat at night
    on the effluent, on the sea,
television out, it crackled, crackling
    [it would have been outside]
[that shard of] yelping, that fuzzy static
    [of sleep's papier-mâché]
and his arm jerk-backed, rolling
    seaward, toward the sea,
muscle gone south, a mouse on the arm of him
    on the sea-slapped arm of him
clapping   [still far away]
    you see, you saw
his robot brain do a brain freeze, dumb
    on mollies in the sea
of bodies, marking his moment of release

when I step out from the music to the silence
and streetlights
each car in the lot intones its color
like a bush cricket honing its wings

you got a sweet boyfriend   woman
    [leaning in, line's dingbat]
his feet patched in like a shrug on their legs,

     lolling on waves in the sun of the strobe,
stacked monitors, sudden condor
     swoop [he mixed his drinks]

once busward from school, guitar going
                            [what]

better make
better make
better make a baby
before it's too late

BOB ELMENDORF

Solstice

I hide in words. That's not where you'll catch me.
Winter, your first sun ducking through the woods,
drops in a well at four, a perfect match for me.

A December maple rounded in fog watches me
from a field of snow, just where I'd have stood.
I hide in words. That's not where you'll catch me.

In this poem you'll find my photograph, scree
at the cliff's bottom, I've done all I could,
drop in a well at four, a perfect match for me.

Or let's settle on a glacial erratic, free
standing on a ledge's rim by granite troughs
whose loose pink feldspar oblongs weather roughly.
I hide in words. That's not where you'll catch me,

better yet in a school of gravel, a swatch warily
under current organized against the flow.
Drop in a well at four, a perfect match for me.

But best of all the math in sand candidly
pouring homeless on the beach. Should
I hide in words, that's not where you'll catch me,
drop in a well at four, a perfect match for me.

Fireflies

Phosphors lessened under the duress of twilight
still blink a dirge for the sidewise fallen rabbit
hit and run and the wet imprint his body made
a shadow no sun could cast a dismal urine bath.
Stars brightened in the pan of developing night
synced too and the rumbling trucks' headlights
tapped harmonic morse among the tree's distant
branches so full of summer leaves each autumn
strips. I gently prodded the body into the weeds
and turned it once again to leave it undisturbed.
I don't ask any more for myself when at the end
wound at last in the swaddling clothes of death
I cannot budge the stone against my tomb.

The Horticulturalist

I was the soldier who stood at attention
as you drilled the asparagus in its bed;
you the tin woman with your watering can
waiting for me to pin a heart beneath your head.

You Barnumed heirlooms through their rippling
hoops, better boys, cherry, early girl, and pear.
I was erratic, you were concentric, crippling
with commands an untamable bear.

You coaxed an elephant from your hutch
etched on the cover of a sterling book
given to your grandfather in India
along with ancient coins he took,

the size I needed for the tiny slots
in the elevator I could not make descend
just the night before in a dream I'd got.
Oneiromancy in romances can't portend.

I was the vine you could not train,
the scion you could not graft.
The lion undeterred by your chair,
the roughened current around your raft.

You were the windy lass in your faux well
hauling me in buckets to water the garden,
a rain barrel the downspouts swelled
softening the ground water hardened

with minerals, fostering your basil hedge.
Smitten with cumulus and the unlettered stars
you lay on your driveway or stood on a ledge
to let go of nears and grab onto fars.

Parthenogenesis

I divided the night into two pockets
leaving the one and entering the other.
I was electric in the dutch door socket.

I was the thread in the needle's rocket
that sewed the dusk and the dawn together.
I divided the night into two pockets,

meandered the seam that stitched charged crochets
switching cheeked hail in a thunder cloud's weather.
I was electric in the dutch door socket,

reversing the current in my two pronged crotches
before I separated from my twin brother.
I divided the night into two pockets

and sired myself, no seed from dad's packet,
in a room of my own without mom's bother.
I was electric in the dutch door socket,

following the char that the lightning botched
into two terminals my acorn fathered.
I divided the night into two pockets.
I was electric in the dutch door socket.

BARRY GIFFORD

Passage on a Slow Freighter

Blaise Cendrars wrote,
Today I am perhaps the happiest man
in the world. I have everything
I don't want.
When I was younger, I could not
have understood this feeling.
Now, three years shy of seventy,
it makes sense, a sentiment
I share, having shed the pride
of possessiveness and, worse,
false necessity. No longer
important to fool myself
or believe my own lies.
It's the sparrow on the windowsill
on a darkening afternoon—
that we both can smell
the fast-approaching rain
is all the belonging I need.

CONTRIBUTORS

MARTIN AITKEN is a translator of Scandinavian literature. His translations include works by Peter Høeg, Jussi Adler-Olsen, Dorthe Nors, Kim Leine, and Pia Juul. He is currently at work translating the sixth book of Karl Ove Knausgaard's *My Struggle* from Norwegian with Don Bartlett.

HOWARD ALTMANN's second book of poems, *In This House*, was published in 2010.

KAREN LEONA ANDERSON is the author of two books of poems, *Punish Honey* and *Receipt*. Her work has appeared in *ecopoetics*, *New American Writing*, *Fence*, *Volt*, and *The Best American Poetry 2012*.

MALCOLM BARRETT is a doctoral student in epidemiology at the University of Southern California and author of the chapbook *Greasefire*. These poems were completed during a residency at the Zen Center of New York City. He now lives in Pasadena, California.

APRIL BERNARD's recent book, *Brawl & Jag*, includes the poems that appear in this issue. She is the author of four previous books of poems and two novels, most recently *Miss Fuller*. She teaches literature and writing at Skidmore College and is on the faculty of the Bennington MFA writing program.

NINA BOGIN's most recent book of poems is *The Lost Hare*. Her translation of Agota Kristof's autobiographical narrative *The*

Illiterate appeared in 2013 with CB Editions, who also published her translations of several of Kristof's short stories in *Sonofabook Magazine*.

MARIN BUSCHEL's work has appeared in *Conjunctions*, *Fence*, *Epoch*, *New Orleans Review*, and *Sleepingfish*.

DAVID COLMER is an Australian translator of Dutch literature. Recent translations include Menno Wigman's *Window-Cleaner Sees Paintings* and Ester Naomi Perquin's *The Hunger in Plain View*, in which this poem appears.

REILLY COSTIGAN-HUMES lives and works in Moscow, where he translates Russian and Ukrainian literature. His translation, with Isaac Stackhause Wheeler, of Serhiy Zhadan's *Mesopotamia* will appear this spring.

TADEUSZ DĄBROWSKI is a poet, essayist, and critic, living in Gdańsk, Poland. He is the editor of the literary bimonthly *Topos* and the art director of the European Poet of Freedom Festival. He has published two books of poems in English, both translated by Antonia Lloyd-Jones, *Black Square* and, most recently, *Posts*, in which these poems appear.

GRO DAHLE has written over thirty books in different genres, including poetry, fiction, and children's books. A book of poems in English, in Rebecca Wadlinger's translation, *A Hundred Thousand Hours*, appeared in 2014. She lives on the Norwegian island of Tjöme.

RON DE MARIS' poems have appeared, most recently, in *Sewanee Review*, *Stand*, and *Southern Review*. His book *36 Elegant Diversions* was published this year.

SASHA DUGDALE is a translator, poet, and playwright. She has translated many works of Russian poetry, prose, and drama, including Tatiana Shcherbina's *Life Without: Selected Poetry & Prose 1992–2003*, Elena Shvarts's *Birdsong on the Seabed*, and Chekhov's *The Cherry Orchard* for BBC Radio. She was until recently the editor of *Modern Poetry in Translation*.

ERICA X EISEN's works have appeared or are forthcoming in *The Threepenny Review*, *Pleiades*, *Salamander*, *The Atticus Review*, *Lumen*, *The Harvard Advocate*, and the *Nivalis 2015* anthology. She lives in Pennsylvania.

BOB ELMENDORF has been published in thirty magazines and has been a member of several poetry workshops. He teaches Catullus, Horace, Lucretius, and Vergil to homeschooling students pro bono.

BARRY GIFFORD is the author of more than forty books, and his film credits include *Wild at Heart*, *Lost Highway*, and *City of Ghosts*. His new book of poems, *New York, 1960 & Other Poems*, in which this poem appears, was published this year.

ELIZABETH T. GRAY, JR. is the author of a book of poems, *Series\India*, and translator of *The Green Sea of Heaven: Fifty Ghazals from the Diwan-i Hafiz-i Shirazi*. She has performed Hafiz's work in concert with Iranian musicians in a number of settings and produced a CD. Her translations of contemporary Iranian poetry can be found in *Iran: Poems of Dissent*. With her colleague Siddiq Wahid, Ms. Gray is currently translating a pre-Buddhist oral version of Tibet's primary folk epic, King Kesar of Ling.

ARIELLE GREENBERG's newest books include a book of poems, *Come Along with Me to the Pasture Now*, and *Locally Made Panties*, a book of prose. She is co-author, with Rachel Zucker, of *Home/Birth: A Poemic* and co-editor of four anthologies. She writes a column on contemporary poetics for *American Poetry Review* and a series for *The Rumpus*. She lives in Maine.

GILES HARVEY is a senior editor at *Harper's Magazine* and a contributing writer at *The New York Times Magazine*.

CYNAN JONES was born near Aberaeron on the west coast of Wales in 1975. He is the author of five novels, *Everything I Found on the Beach, The Dig, Bird, Blood, Snow, Cove,* and *The Long Dry,* in which "The Rabbit" appears.

GEORGE KALOGERIS is the author of a book of paired poems in translation, *Dialogos,* and a book of poems based on the notebooks of Albert Camus, *Camus: Carnets*. His poems and translations appeared in Christopher Ricks' anthology, *Joining Music with Reason*. His most recent book, *Guide to Greece,* in which this poem appears, will be published in 2018.

BOŻENA KEFF is a poet, critic, and essayist. She has conducted literary research at the Jewish Historical Institute in Warsaw and teaches gender studies at Warsaw University and elsewhere. "Persephone" is adapted from her book-length poem, *On Mother and Fatherland*. She is also the author of several critical studies of gender and Polish nationalism.

MICHAEL KIMBALL is the author of eight books, including *Big Ray, Dear Everybody, Us,* and, most recently, *The One-Hour MFA*.

JOSEFINE KLOUGART has written five novels, two of which have appeared in English translation, *Of Darkness* and *One of Us Is Sleeping,* from which this story was drawn. She is also an art and theater critic, the editor of the Danish literary magazine,

Den Blå Port, and one of the founders of the Danish publishing house Forlaget Gladiator.

STEVE KRONEN's books are *Splendor* and *Empirical Evidence*. He is a librarian in Miami.

BRUCE LAWDER has published three books of poems and a book of essays on poetry, *Vers le vers,* as well as numerous articles on painting. In addition to Hölderlin, he has recently translated work by Johannes Bobrowski, Georg Trakl, Paul Celan, and André du Bouchet. He has just completed a musical without music called *Tromp (The Musical)*. He lives in Switzerland.

ANTONIA LLOYD-JONES is a translator from the Polish living in London.

ANTHONY MADRID lives in Victoria, Texas. These poems appear in his second book, *Try Never.*

QUENTIN MAHONEY studied philosophy and mathematics at Evergreen State College in Olympia, Washington. He writes songs and works at a bar.

GLYN MAXWELL is a poet, playwright, and librettist. His selected poems were published in 2011; his most recent book of poems is *Pluto*. He also edited the *The Poetry of Derek Walcott 1948–2013*. His poetry guidebook, *On Poetry*, was published 2012 and was followed by a companion volume, *Drinks With Dead Poets*, from which this excerpt was drawn.

JEAN McGARRY has published nine books of fiction, most recently the book of stories, *No Harm Done*, in which this story appears. She is Elliott Coleman Professor of Fiction in The Writing Seminars at Johns Hopkins University.

JOHN MORAN is a doctoral candidate at Stanford and has published work in *Subtropics*, *Southern Cultures*, and *Little Star*.

LES MURRAY is the author of a dozen books of poetry, most recently *Waiting for the Past*. In 1998 he was awarded the Gold Medal for Poetry, selected by Ted Hughes. His poems have appeared in every issue of *Little Star*. He lives in New South Wales, Australia.

E.O. NESSUNA is a filmmaker and writer.

MICHAEL PALMER is the author of a number of books of poems, most recently *The Laughter of the Sphinx*, from which these poems are drawn. He is the translator of works by Emmanuel Hocquard, Vicente Huidobro, and Alexei Parshchikov, among others, and the editor of *Code of Signals: Recent Writings in Poetics*.

BENJAMIN PALOFF is the author of two books of poems, most recently *And His Orchestra*. He has translated the work of a number of Polish poets.

ESTER NAOMI PERQUIN is a Dutch poet. *The Hunger in Plain View*, her first book in English, in which this poem appears, was published recently in David Colmer's translation.

ROWAN RICARDO PHILLIPS is the author of two books of poems, *The Ground* and *Heaven*, as well as *When Blackness Rhymes with Blackness*, a book of essays, and a translation, from the Catalan, of *Ariadne in the Grotesque Labyrinth*. He writes about sports for *The New Yorker* and *Paris Review*. He lives in New York City and Barcelona.

GLEN POURCIAU's first book of stories won the 2008 Iowa Short Fiction Award. His second book of stories, *View*, appeared this year.

ELLIOT REED's first novel, *A Key to Treehouse Living*, will appear in 2018.

MARY JO SALTER's eighth book of poems, in which these poems appear, is *The Surveyors*. She is Krieger-Eisenhower Professor in The Writing Seminars at Johns Hopkins University, and lives in Baltimore.

TRAVIS SMITH is the author of *Zodiac B*, a chapbook. His poems have appeared in *Crazyhorse*, *Redivider*, and *The Winter Anthology*, among other journals. He lives in Chapel Hill, North Carolina, and works as a bookseller.

MARIA STEPANOVA is the author of twelve books of poems and two books of essays and the founding editor-in-chief of the online Russian cultural magazine *Colta.ru*. She lives in Moscow.

JAMES STOTTS is a poet and translator living in Boston. His work has appeared in *Berfois*, *Agni*, *The Atlantic*, and *The Charles River Journal*. His first book, *Since*, was reissued in 2016 and his second, *Elgin Pelicans*, will be published later this year.

JULIA THACKER's poems and stories have appeared in *Agni*, *Antaeus*, *The Boston Globe Magazine*, *The Massachusetts Review*, *Ms Magazine*, *The North American Review*, *New Directions*, and *The Pushcart Prize Anthology*. She lives in Cambridge, Massachusetts.

AARON THIER is the author of *The Ghost Apple* and *Mr. Eternity*, from which this story is adapted. His third novel, *The*

World is a Narrow Bridge, will be published this spring. He lives in western Massachusetts.

ALISSA VALLES is the editor and co-translator of Zbigniew Herbert's *Collected Poems 1956–1998* and *Collected Prose 1948–1998*.

ERICK VERRAN has work forthcoming in *Gargoyle Magazine* and *The Journal of Pre-Raphaelite Studies*. He is preparing a manuscript for punctum books.

REBECCA WADLINGER is a graduate of the Michener Center for Writers in Austin and the University of Houston's Creative Writing PhD program. She translated Gro Dahle's *A Hundred Thousand Hours*. Her own poems have recently appeared in *Tin House*, *Ploughshares*, *Kenyon Review*, and *The Collagist*.

ROSANNA WARREN's most recent books of poems are *Departure* and *Ghost in a Red Hat*. Her book of criticism, *Fables of the Self: Studies in Lyric Poetry*, came out in 2008. She is at work on a biography of Max Jacob, some parts of which have appeared in *Little Star*. She teaches at the University of Chicago and lives in Chicago.

ISAAC STACKHOUSE WHEELER's translations have appeared in *Two Lines* and *The Missing Slate*, and his poems have appeared in *Coldnoon* and *Three Drops from a Cauldron*. His translation, with Isaac Stackhouse Wheeler, of Serhiy Zhadan's *Mesopotamia* will appear this spring.

ROBERT WRIGLEY is the author of seven books of poems. "Mother Country" appears in his new book, *Anatomy of Melancholy and Other Poems*. He lives in Idaho.

MATT ZAMBITO is the author of *The Fantastic Congress of Oddities* and two chapbooks, *Guy Talk* and *Checks & Balances*. He lives in Spokane, Washington.

SERHIY ZHADAN is a Ukrainian poet, novelist, musician, and activist. His books have twice been named BBC Ukraine's Book of the Year. These passages are drawn from his recently translated novel, *Voroshilovgrad*. His novel *Mesopotamia*, also translated by Reilly Costigan-Humes and Isaac Stackhause Wheeler, will appear in English next spring.

"The Rabbit," by Cynan Jones, first appeared in *The Long Dry*, published by Graywolf Press (2007); "One of Us Is Sleeping," by Josefine Klougart, first appeared in *One of Us Is Sleeping*, published by Open Letter (2016); "Emily Dickinson Lesson," by Glyn Maxwell, first appeared in *Drinks with Dead Poets*, published by Pegasus Books (2017); "Vierge Ouvrante," by Mary Jo Salter first appeared in *The Surveyors*, published by Alfred A. Knopf (2017); "Voroshilovgrad," by Serhiy Zhadan, first appeared in *Voroshilovgrad*, published by Deep Vellum Press (2016); "Try Never," "Pants Pants Pants," and "Four Four Four," by Anthony Madrid, first appeared in *Try Never*, published by Canarium Books (2017); "Found Sonnet: Samuel Johnson," "Werner Herzog in the Amazon," "Samaria," "When I Was Thirteen, I Saw *Uncle Vanya*," and "Trying to Like Spenser," by April Bernard, first appeared in *Brawl & Jag*, published by W.W. Norton (2016); "Nothing Was Made," "The Gargantuan City," and "Shadows," by Tadeusz Dąbrowski, first appeared in *Black Square*, published by Zephyr Press (2011); "Mr. Eternity," by Aaron Thier, first appeared in *Mr. Eternity*, published by Riverhead Books (2016); "Poem Devoid of Meaning" and "Strange Now" by Michael Palmer, first appeared in *The Laughter of the Sphinx*, published by New Directions (2016); "The Baby but One," by Jean McGarry, first appeared in *No Harm Done*, published by Dalkey Archive Press (2017); "Mother Country," by Robert Wrigley, first appeared in *Box*, published by Penguin Books (2017); "Persephone," by Bożena Keff, first appeared in *On Mother and Fatherland*, published by MadHat (2017); "Milky Way," "Music of the Future," "Pelican Island," "Pelican Man," "In the Heart of Old San Juan," "Paramin," and "Lapeyrouse Umbrella," by Derek Walcott first appeared in *Morning, Paramin*, published by Farrar, Straus & Giroux (2017); and "Passage on a Slow Freighter," by Barry Gifford, first appeared in *The Cuban Club*, published by Seven Stories Press (2017). Copyright © 2017 (unless otherwise noted) remains with the authors and translators

WE HOPE YOU HAVE ENJOYED LITTLE STAR #7!

Perhaps you would like a past issue! Or a copy for a friend. You can order *Little Star* with the form below or online at littlestarjournal.com/issues, where we have a complete list of our past authors and pieces. We are also available electronically: full issues of Little Star can be downloaded as PDFs (littlestarjournal.com/issues). Send us your email address to receive announcements and special offers.

attn: Subscriptions
107 Bank Street, New York, NY 10014
info@littlestarjournal.com • www.littlestarjournal.com

Name:				
Address:				
City:		State:	Zip:	
Phone: ( )				
E-mail address:				
Ship to (if different):				
Address:				
City:		State:	Zip:	
Order:				
LITTLE STAR #7	_____ copies	@ $14.95 per copy	Postage and handling: $4.00 domestic, $10.00 international	TOTAL_____
Still available:				
LITTLE STAR #5 (2014)	_____ copies	@ $14.95 per copy	Postage and handling: $4.00 domestic, $10.00 international	TOTAL_____
LITTLE STAR #3 (2013)	_____ copies	@ $14.95 per copy	Postage and handling: $4.00 domestic, $10.00 international	TOTAL_____
			PAYMENT ENCLOSED	$ _____

☐   I'm not ordering today, but please add me to your mailing list.

Insomniac Dreams

Experiments with Time by Vladimir Nabokov

Compiled, edited, and with commentaries by Gennady Barabtarlo

"Nabokov's actual accounts of his dreams . . . are fantastic, and show in raw form the wit, facility, and inherent discipline of language easily recognizable as Nabokov's handiwork. . . . The note cards alone . . . will fortify Nabokov scholars for years to come."
—*Publishers Weekly*

Cloth $24.95

New in the Princeton Series of Contemporary Poets
Susan Stewart, Series Editor

Radioactive Starlings

Poems

Myronn Hardy

"Filled with ecstatic moments, the poems in *Radioactive Starlings* are supreme examples of lyric restraint as well as lush, colorful precision. This compelling collection makes a powerful case for claiming Hardy as one of our finest lyric poets."
—Khaled Mattawa, author of *Tocqueville: Poems*

Paper $17.95
Cloth $45.00

The Unstill Ones

Poems

Miller Oberman

"Magnificent. . . . Anglo-Saxon England and postindustrial America call out to one another across the millennia: casting new-old light on graves, ruins, horses, and words themselves. These are poems to keep close by, to share, and to sing out loud."
—Carolyne Larrington, University of Oxford

Paper $17.95
Cloth $45.00

PRINCETON UNIVERSITY PRESS   press.princeton.edu

THE JOSEPH BRODSKY FELLOWSHIP FUND

*The Joseph Brodsky Memorial Fellowship Fund has been sending
Russian writers and visual artists to Italy for periods of
work and study since 1996. Please help nourish Brodsky's vision of a
flourishing world culture by making this opportunity available to
some of Russia's most forward-thinking artists and intellectuals.*

www.josephbrodsky.org

Sign up now!

For LITTLE STAR 8

littlestarjournal.com

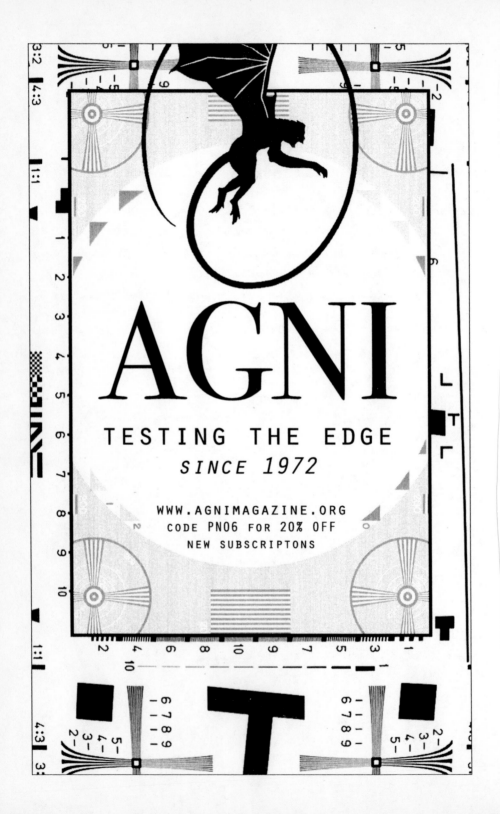

AGNI

TESTING THE EDGE

SINCE 1972

WWW.AGNIMAGAZINE.ORG
CODE PN06 FOR 20% OFF
NEW SUBSCRIPTONS